The Octagonal Heart

Ariadne Thompson

The

Octagonal

Heart

Drawings by ARTUR MAROKVIA

THE WEBSTER GROVES BOOKSHOP
PUBLISHERS

TO JOHN PETER, WITH LOVE

The

Octagonal

Heart

Contents

Prologue

WHEN we were children, we used to spend our summers and all of our holidays at my aunt's house, which
was called Parnassus after the ancient mountain of
the Muses, according to Greek mythology. This small
estate, consisting of about thirty acres of cultivated
land, was situated outside St. Louis in the suburb of
Webster Groves.

For us, coming by streetcar from the city, the first
sight of the long driveway bordered by evergreen
trees was a moment of delight. We felt at once that
lighthearted freedom that invades the heart whenever
regularity and conformity are temporarily dismissed.
Jogging along in the surrey that always met us at the
station, we would crane our necks to see the countryside. And the sight of the house, rising elaborately
and fancifully in the midst of so many trees and

11

flowers, had a fairyland quality that quickened our hearts, although my brother had invariably been carsick, and Mama would insist on putting him to bed at once as he looked "green around the gills."

The house is long since gone, and in the place where it once stood, surrounded by landscaped lawns and fruitful orchards, by rolling pasture and fertile farmland, there now flourishes that new development indigenous to the American countryside known as the subdivision. In the place where violets grew beside a brook and cattails waded in the water, where chestnut trees covered the ground with their prickly burrs, and in all the cool, still, dark places where we first discovered toadstools and lichen moss and angleworms, there now stand ranch houses. Against the sky where we used to watch to see Apollo's Flock—the soft, white clouds that gather together in the sky before sundown —television antennae now form their jagged patterns.

The outbuildings are all gone, too: the laundry house with its black iron tubs of steamy water and the vats of thick boiled starch and the flatirons heating on the stove—the huge barn with its sweet summer smell of new-mown hay and the other smell we loved so well of manure and leather and horses' sweat. Here among the harnesses and saddles, the pitchforks and the grindstone, the everyday, workaday implement of labor, stood Mercury, a beautiful sleigh, arched and curved like a lady's slipper, painted dark red and ornamented with the golden wings of the god of speed. Mercury poised for flight among the plows and scythes, its bells stilled, its shafts empty . . . These are all gone, along with the chicken house, the carriage house, the playhouse and the cowsheds lined with pails of warm, foamy milk against which we used to lay our cheeks. . . .

And the main house is gone, with its great octagonal entrance hall, an open well rising four stories to the cupola above, each floor surrounded by an interior balcony from which hung a bronze fringe, decorated with colored balls and golden acorns. And all its magic rooms are gone: the Billiard Room and the Wine Room—Thea's room with its secret bed and the parlor and the pantry and the Medicine Room—the attic rooms, crammed with trunks and toys and treasures—and down, down, down beneath the cellar, beneath the earth itself, entered only through a tunnel, the Storm Room.

It is all gone now, lost to us these many years, and there is nothing of it left to see with the eyes or feel with the hand or touch or hear with any part of the body save the heart. But in the heart it has remained, and I will tell you about this house and all the people in it, and how it shaped the heart of childhood.

Parnassus

THE house was octagonal in shape and made of olive-green shingles lavishly trimmed with the fancy fret-work so fashionable in Victorian houses of the early century. Inside, my cousins, Aphrodite, Achilles, Demosthenes and Aristotle were in their separate rooms, for it was summer and they were not in college. Outside, Mama and Auntie reclined in the hammocks under the flowering chestnut trees.

I lay in my bed in the spare room, where I had been told to take a nap with my brother and sister. Mama, who had a fetish about sallow skin and refused to believe ours was the natural olive color of the Greeks, had warned us to go right to sleep lest we turn to Chinamen. This astonishing precaution had the effect of putting my sister and brother into an instant coma,

14

but I, doubting any such possibility, lay wide-awake, listening to a bee buzz against the screen, impatient with this hour of confinement.

I turned to look at my sister and brother. Artemis' mouth was opened a little, making a sweet oval in her moon-shaped face, and her light-brown hair lay across the pillow like a fan. In the next bed Pericles dreamed. They both had the heavy lids that give people of our nationality a somnolent look even when awake, and in their sleep they seemed remote, wholly isolated and lost to me forever.

For a while I just lay there, waiting for the hour to end, listening to a lawn mower churn across the grass with recurring and diminishing sounds, now and then hearing Hercules, the Saint Bernard dog, grumble as someone walked across a gravel path. The sounds teased me, for I longed to be outdoors, and idle thoughts, like dust dancing in sunlight, scattered through my mind. Would cousin Aphrodite really have to marry a Greek . . .? Why was this important? It seemed to overlay everything, like a vague shadow, at Parnassus. Sometimes everyone in the house talked about it at once and Aphrodite always cried and went up to her room, like a princess locked in a tower. And at these times my beautiful auntie's profile was hostile, so that no one dared talk to her and she went about with her lips pressed together and her eyebrows raised like two flags unfurled. Once I heard Papa say that Auntie regarded Greek culture exactly as she regarded her liver; something one could not do without and over which one must keep constant vigil lest it grow sluggish. When he said this, he laughed and I wondered what it meant.

Tired of this unsolvable problem, I turned to another, equally mysterious. Was it true that from the cupola one could really see both Webster Groves and Kirkwood, a neighboring suburb?

On an impulse I decided to investigate. This was mutiny, for we had been forbidden ever to enter the cupola alone lest the height make us dizzy and we topple from the balcony. Mama had used dire language and even reminded us of Phaethon, son of Helios, who had insisted on driving the sun's chariot against the better judgment of the gods. As a result the horses had dashed furiously away, frightening the constellations as they madly raced uncontrolled up and down the heavens. The sky was threatened with conflagration, the clouds smoked and burned the hills beneath, turning all the Ethiopians black, and Phaethon was cast down from the sky, screaming, into the river Eridanus. After this his seven sisters had mourned until their tears turned to amber.

In spite of this object lesson I crept out of bed in my nightgown and made my way up to the third floor and to the foot of the spiral staircase, which led to the forbidden cupola above. This small structure was set like a crown atop the octagonal house and indeed it looked much like a crown with each of its eight windows paned in different colored glass and the fancy weather vane piercing its peak like a star.

At the foot of the staircase I looked above and faltered. The stairs were narrow, the height dizzying.

These obstacles, plus the fact I was acting against the sternest warnings from Mama and Auntie, caused me to ponder. But only for a moment, for in the next instant I flew up the steps like barefoot Diana and stood at last on the highest pinnacle I had ever known.

My heart seemed to stop. One could, indeed, see both Kirkwood and Webster Groves. The world lay beneath me, spread out in a green and golden pattern. I saw Mama and Auntie in their hammocks under the chestnut trees and over the way, in the fields, the hired men making brown, corrugated paths with their plows. I saw the barns, the chicken houses, the stables and, beyond all this, the streets and houses of the villages forming a checkered pattern as far as the eye could reach. I saw a woman hanging out her wash a long way off, and a man, opening his front door, stooped to pick up a paper.

The peculiar sensation of seeing into other people's lives without their knowing it produced the effect on me of a kind of omniscience. We had never read American nursery rhymes, but instead were given books of Greek mythology, and I felt truly that I was a goddess atop Mount Olympus, monitoring the destiny of the mere mortals beneath. I thought of Echo, who dared talk back to the goddess Hera and was forthwith turned into a voice, committed forever to repeat other people's words. I thought of Arachne, turned into a spider because her pride in her weaving galled the gods, and the idea of such mystical power thrilled me.

As I stood there in the cupola I was much too

young, being only six years old, to comprehend the great, complex, anomalous quality of the ancient Greek mythology, nor could I have understood its many profiles. I only knew the gods were relentless in exercising their authority, and I was much impressed with the swift and inexorable punishments which befell all who did not toe the mark according to their precepts. Like avenging angels wearing the face of wrath, they turned mortals into stags, boars and stones without a moment's hesitation. Remembering this, I turned my eyes to Mama and Auntie with such superiority as I had never known before.

They reclined in the hammocks, drinking coffee and talking in Greek. They wore the flowing gowns they put on every afternoon when they wandered in the gardens or had their coffee beneath the trees. These were made in the style of the classical Greek gown called a chiton and were of a thin, white cotton material, crossed over the breast and twice around the waist by a silk cord. Their hair was caught with bands of silken ribbon high off the neck in Psyche style, and on their feet they wore golden sandals. Remembering the injustice of having been put to bed to take a nap, I was about to turn them into shadows, condemned to sleep through all the golden hours of the day, only to rise and walk as the sun died down, when a most joyous thing occurred.

From far away down the road I saw my Uncle Demetrius galloping on his horse, riding hard upon the house with a sack over his back. In a transport of delight I flew down the spiral staircase and rushed to awaken my sister and brother as I heard Auntie gasp, "*Ach Theo Mu!*" (which means "Oh, my God!" in Greek) as she and Mama ran into the house.

Undaunted by the stark tragedy in her voice, I called Artemis and Pericles and all three of us ran downstairs to the entrance hall just as Mama and Auntie were furiously and wildly removing all breakable objects from view.

Auntie, clutching a Sevres vase, thrust it at Artemis as soon as she saw her, extolling its value and telling her to put it in the dining room.

"Ariadne! Pericles!" she exhorted, handing us various *objets d'art*. "Put these in the parlor!" She herself rushed to the library with a bisque statuette of a little boy in lavender pantaloons and a glass globe which encased an arrangement of wax flowers.

Mama collected everything she could lay her hands on and removed them to safety. Then, always worrying about health and bodily injury, tried ineffectually to clasp us to her bosom when in the door roared Uncle Demetrius, the horse tied safely outside, the sack over his back. Up and up the stairs he went, like a little gnome, looking neither here nor there. Up and up, past the first balcony, past the second until he reached the third where, leaning over and shouting, "Yi, Yi, down there! Scramble now! Here come the presents!" he emptied his bag and showered down upon us pennies, nuts, candies and a whole collection of enchanting, miniature toys. Down they came, clattering and bouncing and scattering every which way and all three of us ran and laughed and shouted as we picked up the treasures—while Mama and Auntie stood on in a kind of resigned despair and Aphrodite, Achilles, Demosthenes and Aristotle—once themselves the recipients of such bounties, now superior in their status of seniority—came out of their rooms and looked down with a shrug.

Lightning in the Sky

EIGHT people lived in the octagonal house. There were my aunt and uncle, their four children, Aphrodite, Achilles, Demosthenes and Aristotle, my grandfather, who officiated at the Greek Orthodox Church which he founded in St. Louis and Thea, who had once been governess to my cousins.

Of our four cousins, Demosthenes was the one we loved most dearly, for he was imaginative and gentle and at the same time filled our lives with a kind of mysterious excitement. Sometimes he would take walks with us, and on these occasions he always carried a butterfly net, darting away now and then to capture a Pearly Eye or a Monarch.

He was tall and thin with a kind of Byronic face, both sensitive and beautiful, and he loved nature and was forev r awed by the things that God had made.

I suppose this was because Demosthenes was an inventor and saw in God's handiwork the epitome of intricate grace and construction. His own room was filled with blueprints of the most elaborate laborsaving devices—lights that turned on and off without a switch, doors that opened without a touch and even a machine to wash dishes. The entire family considered him eccentric in this way, but everyone approved his nearness to God and his love of nature.

On our walks Demosthenes was always collecting things—the empty, papery, brown shell of a locust, a dead bee, a bird's egg or a bit of lichen moss—and these he would carefully place in his pocket for examination under the miscroscope when we returned to the house. With each treasure he unfolded a tale, and Artemis, Pericles and I were enraptured. He told us about the great swarms of locusts in India which make a summer sky as dark as night and arrive with a thundering sound like a herd of buffalo to strip the land of all vegetation. He told us about the crickets in China and Japan that are kept in cages, like canaries, to delight their owners with their song. And often he stopped and knelt before an anthill under a grove of pine trees, describing to us the wonders therein.

Demosthenes taught us many things and filled our summer days and nights with magic. Walking along with Hercules, the Saint Bernard dog, ambling at our heels, he showed us how a butterfly's wings form a perfect, identical pattern on both sides as if one had been painted, then folded over to leave its imprint on the other. He told us stories of the meteors and comets, and he taught us to feel a cat purr.

But most of all, I think, we were captivated by his inventions. We loved to look at the blueprints etched all over with white lines like fairy castles in the sky, and, while his elaborate symposiums on the quantum theory and the speed and activity of molecules were lost to us, we were fascinated by his descriptions of mysterious machines that would interpret in foreign languages what was typed in English, and machines that would bring moving pictures to our house with the flip of a switch and music dancing over the airways to be heard in the parlor at the very moment it was playing at the opera house.

He was then in his late teens, the oldest of our cousins and by far the most imaginative. When he was a grown man he invented and patented, among other things, an image-detecting device which could automatically convert common printed matter into Braille symbols under the finger of the blind as they moved it across the pages—but in the years when we were children and he a boy, some of his inventions were less practical.

He was a bug for safety and was constantly inventing devices for us to use in the event a robber waylaid us on a dark street and said, "Hands up!" One of these was a kind of tube worn across the shoulders and down through the sleeves, on the ends of which were rubber atomizers which could be clasped in each hand. At the moment we were accosted we were to raise our

arms and at the same time squeeze the atomizers, thus blinding our assailant with the pepper contained therein.

Mama was very much annoyed when she heard about this invention. She said Demosthenes was putting ideas in our heads, and besides we never walked alone on dark streets at night. She was so upset that Papa said, *"Apheseto Pythie mu,"* which means "Never mind, darling" in Greek. This was the only time Mama ever had a quarrel with Demosthenes, for she loved him dearly and was the only one who believed his inventions would work. To compensate for refusing to let us wear the tube, she did not say a word when he cautioned us never to sign our names to a piece of paper lest a villain insert a promise to pay a large sum of money in the space above, for which we would then be liable. Aristotle, who was studying law, got into the act and said that that was absurd, but Mama only said, "Sh-h-h-h."

Another time Demosthenes took us aside and advised us never to let strange men buy us ice-cream sodas lest they divert our attention while they poured a potion into the drink which would render us insensible, after which they would carry us off to the white-slave market. We said nothing at all about this to Mama, knowing perfectly well there is much truth in the saying, *"Lega loya taw kalleteron,"* which means, "The least said the soonest mended."

Demosthenes was ever in search of a pure maiden lady to be his wife, but this quest was temporarily interrupted by the advent of the First World War.

The strange, remote detachment of childhood, which serves as an armor against cataclysmic events, has left this period of world upheaval marked only by a vague impression of the boys leaving and the boys coming home, between which Mama and Auntie and Thea wrapped bandages and we were all put to binding the ends of rope with waxed string, which served some purpose in the tents Uncle Demetrius manufactured and sent overseas.

I do remember a particular day when Demosthenes and his brother Achilles sat on either side of their mother on the South Porch. They sat in a swing suspended from the ceiling by two iron chains, and as Demosthenes touched the floor with the toe of his boot to keep the swing in motion, I noticed that he wore khaki puttees, which were wound round his legs like bandages. When I looked at Auntie, her face was set and stony and her eyes were red from weeping, but Achilles and Demosthenes both smiled faintly and kept patting her hands. I felt that without doubt my cousin had a secret invention to blow up the Germans, and I wanted to ask him about it, but it seemed an occasion for silence.

I remember we heard a great deal about the Turks and a man named Mustapha Kemal, who, it appeared, was a personal enemy of Mama's and Auntie's. Whenever they spoke of him, their eyes took on a glassy quality and their voices shook. Papa and Uncle Demetrius argued that the Gallipoli Campaign was only a small part of the World War, but Mama and Auntie,

who always referred to the Seat of Democracy and Two
Thousand Years of Culture in the same breath they
mentioned Greece, hated the Turks for the oppression
of their country. So it was that no amount of propa-
ganda about the Germans could infuriate them half
so much as the mere mention of Mustapha Kemal,
whom I recall envisioning as a man with a yellow face,
black beetle eyes and long, Oriental mustaches over a
leering, evil mouth.

The rope-tying and Mustapha Kemal and a few
songs are all that remain of the war in my memory until the day the boys came home. Then I was standing
on Lindel Boulevard in St. Louis with my sister and
brother in a crowd so dense and we all so small that
all we could see were the tramping boots of soldiers as
they came marching home. Mama and Papa were
there and, of course, my Aunt Elene and Uncle Demetrius. Auntie was crying again and waving her
handkerchief, and a few days later everything went
on as usual at Parnassus.

Demosthenes' attitude toward God and Nature had
not been marred by his close contact with the Turks
(despite Mama's and Auntie's misgivings) and one day
when clouds were gathering in the sky, he took us to
the Storm Room to seek shelter. This small area, built
below the cellar, was carved out of solid rock so that
it was an indomitable fortress against tornado or hur-
ricane and was entered by a long, dark tunnel. High
above the shelter there was a single window, for the
arched ceiling rose to the earth above and formed a hill

over which grass grew—and it was always a surprise to visitors strolling about the property to come across this small hill with a window in its side.

Down in the Storm Room we would climb a high ladder and look out at the rain-slashed world, the birch trees curved against the wind, the willows dripping their long, wet branches like women washing their hair. Through the windowpane, shimmering with water, the sky would be dark and menacing as thunder and lightning ripped it asunder.

Frightened and fascinated, we would climb down from our perch and huddle around our cousin while this gentle soul, in order to soothe us, explained that lightning was only the sky opening now and again to allow us to see the blinding light of God's kingdom within.

A Glass of Pudding

WHEN Demosthenes and Achilles went away to fight in the First World War, we children found much solace in the company of our cousin Aristotle, who was still in his teens and therefore too young for service. Mama, who was forever extolling the Glories That Once Were Greece, had naturally explained to us the mythological and historical backgrounds of our own and our relatives' names, including, of course, Aristotle. I remember trying to associate the qualities of each with those of his namesake.

This required, at times, quite a stretch of the imagination when I tried to relate my uncle Themistocles, for example, with Themistocles the Statesman. Mama's brother was very kind and sensitive, with the softest of voices and the gentlest of hearts, while his historical

29

counterpart had been aggressive, domineering, impassioned and loquacious, as zealous in peace as he was in war. Moreover, my uncle was gentlemanly in his manner and meticulous in his tastes, while his antecedent had eaten and drunk robustly, often saying that the wildest colts make the best horses.

Sometimes I would fix my dark eyes on my uncle as he sat playing the piano, the lamplight falling on his brown, wavy hair, his thin, aquiline nose in profile and his mobile mouth forming the words of a sweet love song. At these times I was hard put to it to imagine him drinking bull's blood, as Mama had told us the other Themistocles had done, rather than fight with the Persians against the Greeks.

The first Aristotle, whom we knew to have been called Seeker After Truth, seemed more like our cousin, for Aristotle was studying law and was ever in search of evidence. Whenever a dispute arose among us, he would call us into his "chambers," which might be the hayloft, the garden wall or his own bedroom, and there, fitting fact to logic to law, come to an indisputable verdict. He was self-imposed judge, jury, sleuth and attorney, and I must say he most efficiently settled many a hassle about a book or a toy or whose turn it was to play with the beautiful, pink shell in the parlor which, when held to the ear, made a mournful sound of the sea.

Another object we often quarreled about was a heavy glass paperweight containing the small figure of a girl standing in the snow. When this was moved or turned about a bit, the snow flurried all around her in a raging storm, leaving her immobile in its midst. Sometimes when Auntie and Uncle Demetrius had celebrated callers, such as Burton Holmes or Isadora Duncan, we were allowed to go into the parlor and sit on one of the carved chairs, each upholstered in a different color, blue, gold, green and red, our feet crossed at the ankles and our hands folded in our laps in a manner considered appropriate for children. There was nothing to play with in the parlor except the little paperweight, for the room was very formal and consisted of stiff furniture, Dresden china and potted ferns. To give us something to do while we were being seen and not heard, Auntie would hand one or the other of us the little paperweight as she went on talking with her guests. Then what an undercurrent of violence would ensue amongst us, for whoever was handed the weight first would clench it in his fists and refuse to give it up. There we would sit, as prim and proper as you please, our eyes cast down in modest self-effacement, while under our fake smiles we gnashed our teeth and beneath the folds of our clothing we punched and pummeled one another in order to gain possession of the treasure. When the guests left, the feud would be carried out into the open, and it would be then that our cousin would be called upon to arbitrate the issue.

In settling these disputes Aristotle used many words and phrases whose meaning we did not understand, but whose very intonation spelled doom. He spoke of statute law, civil, common and criminal law, property rights and circumstantial evidence. And if he met with any opposition at all he simply announced that he could have us all behind bars within twenty minutes, which froze us into a kind of mute docility.

We couldn't get away with anything with Aristotle anyway, for when he fixed us with his dark eyes under heavy brows nearly meeting in a frown, his sharp nose seeming to point into our very souls and his lips pressed together in indignation, he was the very picture of the seeker after truth, and we would confess our guilt, whatever it might be, rather than buck the All-Knowing.

There were times when he settled disputes in other ways, as well. One day when we were all three playing together we simultaneously came upon a lovely, lost object, a small metal pencil in the shape of a bullet with an American flag painted on its side. This seemed the most desirable prize in the whole world, and we all clamored loudly for its possession. In fact, in tears and rage we set upon each other bodily when Aristotle came upon us and elected himself arbiter of the dispute.

He settled it thus. Taking a wooden croquet ball out to the barn, he drilled a hole in its side, placed the pencil in the hole and filled it over with plaster of Paris. The entire mechanics of the operation enchanted us; moreover, we had no idea what the outcome would be. When the pencil was buried inside the croquet ball, its beautiful bullet shape lost to us forever, Aristotle made a circuitous round of the property, taking a pencil and paper with him and mapping out his path—so many steps north from the front door to the arbor, a sharp left turn west from the arbor to the linden tree, due south twenty steps—until he reached the dead center of a rose bed, where he dug down a foot or two and planted the wooden ball.

When it was covered over, he pounded a stake into the ground and informed us that in twenty years we could dig it up, at which time, he trusted, we would be able more equitably to manage our emotions. He then told us something of the teachings of Socrates, who deemed the invisible to be greater than the visible, and informed us that whichever of us had gained possession of the bullet would have forgotten it in a few days. But, this way, we would remember it all of our lives.

No truer words were ever spoken, for to this day, nearly forty years later, I can say to my sister or brother at any time, "I know something you've forgotten all about," and they will answer without hesitation, "The Bullet."

I think Auntie, who loved us dearly and spoiled us unconscionably during our summer vacations, might have objected to what she considered Aristotle's rigid discipline had he not always added a Greek explanation to his rulings. But when he embroidered his sternest judgments with the teachings of Socrates or the precepts of Plato, her expression changed from distress to pleasure.

I am sure our cousin wore the ordinary clothes of a young man of his generation, but in recalling those early days of our childhood, I see him only in the flowing robes of a magistrate. He was Authority, The Law,

the Last Word. And we took our irreconcilable diffi-
culties to him as innocently as the ancient Athenians
took theirs to the gods of the temples.

He was, in our opinion, a most lenient and kindly
judge. And sometimes, when the sessions in his chambers were over and a verdict reached, he would indulge us with a "glass of pudding." This consisted of
the yolks of four eggs beaten with sugar and a fillip
of brandy, which was mixed together in a glass and
eaten with a spoon. When Mama heard about the
brandy, she said, *"Psychi mu!"* which means "My soul!"
in Greek, and fainted.

The Goddess of Washington University

THERE were two sleeping porches at Parnassus: one which the boys used in the summer and another which my aunt and uncle, we three children and our cousin Aphrodite occupied. As Mama and Papa only came out on week ends, Auntie would say our prayers with us, and we three, kneeling in the middle of our beds, would utter, in monotone, the Lord's Prayer in Greek. When Mama came, she would take Auntie's place, but regardless of who officiated at these devotions, we were expected thereafter to go straight to sleep.

As soon as we were alone I would say a prayer in English—one which took me some time to devise, but which I felt encompassed, in one sweeping composition, every possible blight that could conceivably befall me or my fellow man. It went like this:

Dear God, please take care of everybody in the world. Don't let anybody in the world get blind, deaf, dumb, lame, paralyzed or crazy, walk in their sleep or be kidnaped or wake up in the middle of the night with a bad dream. Don't let anybody tell a lie or kill somebody and, if anybody dies, take them up to heaven and please, dear God, take me.

Thus leaving no loopholes and clearly pointing out to our Creator the *modus operandi* by which He could best protect mankind, I felt content and at peace with the world.

It was often difficult to go to sleep at once, for I lacked the literal quality of Artemis and Pericles who, when given instruction, accepted it as immutable. Pericles always went to sleep first, closing his eyes with the calm resignation that was part of his nature. In the half-light I could see his face. His hair was light brown and cut in a Dutch bob so that, with his head back against the pillow, the bangs would part a little on his forehead, giving him a sweet and pious look. To add to the effect of piety, he always lay with his hands clasped on his chest as if in prayer, and his heavy-lidded eyes, when closed, appeared downcast in deep and reverent contemplation. I felt sure he would grow up to be a priest, like my grandfather, and somehow the fact that he had a weak stomach added to my impression of his holiness.

Artemis, who was seven, and the oldest of us three, had long, chestnut-colored hair. She had the same dreamy eyes and a face filled with naïveté and wonder. She gazed, rather than saw, her eyes shining with a

kind of incredulous awe at almost anything she observed. And even now, lying in her bed, I could see
her contemplating the stars as if they had never been
there before.

"Let's tell a story," I whispered, rising up on one
arm.

"Sh-h-h-h," she said. "You know we have to go to
sleep." And in a little while I could hear her snoring
gently, making a funny, little purring sound in her
throat.

But even Artemis and Pericles could not go to sleep
at once on week ends when Mama and Papa were
there. Then we would wait until the family gathered
on the lawn and, after creeping from our beds, would
crouch with our cheeks against the screen and listen
to them singing and talking in the darkness. Mama
had a beautiful coloratura soprano voice and often
sang arias from the great operas with the St. Louis
Symphony Orchestra. But on these occasions, accompanied by Auntie on the guitar, she sang Greek folk
songs in which everyone joined. The songs had a
minor, plaintive quality, like gypsy music, and the
haunting strains seemed to float up to us on the summer night.

In the darkness we could see Mama and Auntie in
their white chitons and, sitting on the grass, leaning
back on their elbows, Achilles, Demosthenes and Aristotle in their white summer trousers and shirts. Thea
would be there and, now and then, Aphrodite
and a young man. Sometimes my grandfather would
be present, nearly indistinguishable in his black

priest's robes, but I could see his pale, long hair flowing over his shoulders and his ghostly, white beard. He always sat a little apart from the group in a tall-backed wicker chair with wheels on it, which he could propel about as if, in his holiness, he must needs remain always a little aloof.

As they sang, fireflies flickered, making dancing lights in the darkness, as gay as the fragments of laughter that interspersed the singing. Mama had a beautiful laugh, melodious and sweet as the songs she sang, and she would put her head back against Papa's shoulder whenever anyone told a joke, and the enchanting sound would come lilting up to us. Papa always held Mama's hand and called her Dearest, for they were very much in love and remained so until the day he died.

After a time the grownups would drift into the house for coffee or a game of billiards and we would, perforce, go back to our beds. Lying there, I felt an immense peace and comfort. The soft summer night was laden with the fragrance of honeysuckle, and the dark sky was pinpricked with stars. I would lie still under the coverlet, my hands at both sides, my heart filled with contentment as I listened. Crickets made a *clickety-click* in the grass, and now and then I could hear the far-off croak of a frog in the pond. Sometimes a dog would bark over the hills, or I could hear the long *whoo-whoo* of a train whistle miles away. And there was the over-all sound of insects in the air, part of the darkness, part of night. I just listened, as

Demosthenes had taught me to do, and night made an insect sound that was ubiquitous and eternal.

In the calm and trusting innocence of childhood, I would drift away to sleep. Usually I slept soundly until morning, but now and again Cousin Aphrodite would bring her best friend, Jenny Brentwood, to spend the night, and then I would sometimes awaken to hear them giggling and talking in their bed next to mine. This afforded me some thrilling moments of eavesdropping as, pretending to be asleep, I listened to their girlish conversations. At this time Aphrodite was having a hard go of it with her mother over the question of dates.

"I think I am old enough," said Aphrodite, who was twenty-two, "to go out with a man alone." She was whispering to Jenny who was whispering back assent. Many young men came to call on Aphrodite, but it was nearly impossible for her to see any of them alone. "Mama and Papa even walk behind us when we take a stroll," she confided.

"That's purely Greek," said Jenny, in sympathy.

"Do you know what happened on Sunday?" asked Aphrodite. "I was never so humiliated in all my life. Ben came out, all the way from the city, and Mama made Achilles and Demosthenes sit on the porch with us the whole time! They were just as embarrassed as I was, and finally it began to rain. I was trying to keep up some kind of conversation, but you can imagine how I felt! Ben looked bored and the boys looked miserable and no one could think of anything to say.

Finally the rain stopped, and I said, 'Well, I see the sun is coming out,' and what do you think Ben said? Oh, Jenny, I thought I'd die!"

"What did he say?"

"He said, 'Yes, *all* the *sons* are out today!' "

Jenny laughed in the darkness.

"Well, I feel sorry for you," she said. "I really do. It's purely Greek."

"That's true," admitted Aphrodite. "And Mama wants me to marry a Greek man, and I don't think I want to. And anyhow you know it's impossible to know *who* you want to marry unless you're with him alone."

"Naturally," said Jenny.

"I'm not complaining," said Aphrodite, who was complaining bitterly. "Mama is always talking about what a wonderful heritage we have, and I know she's right, but now that we're grown up she doesn't understand we want our independence."

"Naturally," said Jenny.

"Girls didn't have any independence in Greece. And then there's another thing. Grandfather lives with us, and he's even more old-fashioned than Mama. Even if she'd relent a little on some things, he wouldn't. He was really the one who decided which of Mama's suitors was acceptable and who she should marry. It's lucky for her she loved Papa because he was Grandfather's choice."

"What about your father?" asked Jenny. "Is he strict, too?"

"Well, he goes along with Mama in most things,"

Aphrodite explained. "But he's much more American in his ideas. He's in business, you know, and he sees life. When I told him I wanted to be a doctor, he didn't say anything much. He believes in education. But Mama had a fit. I mean it, Jenny. She just couldn't understand it at all. I don't know how I'll ever be able to convince her it's the one thing I want to do more than anything in the world. I'd be a *good* doctor, but Mama thinks it's practically immoral."

She paused for a moment and thought over her plight before she added, "Aunt Penelope's on my side. She's much more *modern* in her ideas." She looked over at us in our beds, the lucky children of Aunt Penelope. "*They'll* never have to go through what I do," she said. "Penelope is ten years younger than Mama, and she came to this country when she was eight years old. She's strict but she has modern ideas. I've talked to her a lot, and at least she believes I ought to be allowed to go out with a man alone, without my brothers tagging along. Would you believe it, Jenny, Mama insists I come straight home from college every day. She lives in deadly fear I'm going to meet a man after school!"

"That's purely Greek," said Jenny in sympathy. "I'd put my foot down."

"You can't put your foot down with Mama," said Aphrodite, tragically. "When it comes to things like that, she's made of stone. She's afraid I'll fall in love with an American, and that's all there is to it."

"Well, I feel sorry for you," said Jenny in the darkness. "I really do. Still, I must admit the men flock around you. I don't know why. If my brother tagged along when I went out, they'd run a mile."

Aphrodite sighed.

"Well, Mama thinks I ought to sit home and play the piano and paint and sew and wait for some nice Greek man to come along and marry me. She doesn't think it's ladylike to do anything else. She says she was sitting home painting and sewing when Papa came along, and she's had a beautiful life."

"That's purely Greek," said Jenny who had got into a purely conversational rut. She turned over to go to sleep.

I weighed these things in my mind—what it meant to be purely Greek and how my adorable Auntie could be made of stone. I felt the same old pull that underlay everything at Parnassus, and though I did not understand it, it saddened me. Despite this fact, I felt I was on the track of some very good secrets, especially since they concerned Cousin Aphrodite, who was, in my opinion, the most beautiful and fascinating creature on earth.

She was tall and dark with the true, full figure of a goddess. When she walked, she took long strides and moved with an easy grace. I could well imagine her standing with her foot on a shell or in a chariot drawn by two swans, as the ancient Greeks had done. There was about her a full-blown look, like a ripe peach, and a glow of health that was an aura. She had blue-black hair with a deep wave and dark-brown eyes flecked with gold under brows as sleek and curved as a raven's wing. Her nose, above her rose-red lips, was pure

and carved, tilting a little upward with slightly dilated
nostrils. I think she knew she was beautiful. I doubt
if she could help knowing it, since people everywhere
remarked on her appearance and painters and pho-
tographers beseeched her to pose for her picture. It
was in no way astonishing that her close friends called
her the Goddess of Washington University.

Yet for all her beauty, her one desire was to be a
doctor. And this was understandable, too, since there
was something earthy and basic about her, as if nature
and its principles were clearly defined in her mind.
In many ways she was like her father: forthright, intelligent and blessed with glowing health.

But she was also extremely feminine and even girlish at times. She had closets of beautiful clothes,
drawers of beribboned lingerie and bottles of lotions
and cologne. She had a tiny box of pink rouge which
Mama had given her, but which she did not dare use.
(Mama was indeed far more modern than Auntie
and not only used rouge on her cheeks but had been
known to rub it into her lips.)

We loved to gather round and watch her while she
dressed, and I think we felt that if we were ever to dis-
cover anything about true love and romance it would
be here in Cousin Aphrodite's bedchamber, where she
kept letters tied with blue ribbon locked away in a
drawer, along with a diary marked PRIVATE and a few
snapshots of herself with young men.

One day while she was out, we went into her room,
as was our custom, and dressed up in all her clothes.
Pericles put on a pair of black patent-leather high

shoes with gray suede tops and black buttons and Louis heels and swathed himself in a gray suit with squirrel collar. Artemis wore a purple broadcloth dress trimmed with satin in the popular shade known as "*très moutard*" (mustard) and a hat with a polly clamped to its side. I chose green net with trailing butterfly sleeves and a hat with pink roses on the brim.

While prancing up and down before the pier glass with our hands on our hips and making simpering sounds, which we believed to be reasonable facsimiles of the voices of grownups, we soon discovered she had left unlocked the drawer where she kept her diary, letters and snapshots.

I have never decided whether children are natural vandals or born enthusiasts. At any rate, we pounced on the drawer and its contents. The diary was locked, the letters intricately tied with blue ribbon—but the snapshots were loose. When we picked them up, we found one which, to say the least, stopped us dead in our tracks. It was of Aphrodite and a young man. His face was turned away from the camera, but he plainly had both arms around her while her head rested against his chest.

We were stunned. We felt we had come upon a staggering secret. We shut the drawer as if hot coals had burned our fingers and hastily took off the borrowed garments. Then we ran from the room all the way downstairs, out the front door, across the lawn and down the gravel path to the barn, where, hidden in the hayloft, we discussed the snapshot in breathless whispers.

"Did you see?" whispered Artemis, eyes round as moons. "He had his arms around her!"

"Her head was right on his chest!" Pericles recalled. "I bet they're in love!"

"Then he's kissed her!" I cried, clapping my hand over my mouth.

We all considered this, thunderstruck. Then Artemis, ever practical, said, "I wonder if he's Greek. . . ."

"Gosh," said Pericles. "He better be."

"Just think," said I, the budding lady novelist, "they're madly in love. And they can't tell. It's a secret because he's an American and if Auntie knew she would send him away. They're very sad but they meet secretly and kiss."

What was our disappointment, therefore, to what abysmal depths of mortification did we descend, when a few days later, calm as a camel, Aphrodite showed the picture to Mama and us, neatly pasted in her album. Underneath, plainly written in white ink was:

Achilles and I. 1916.

The Heel of Achilles

ACHILLES was the least handsome of the boys but in some ways the most buoyant. To be with him was to rejoice, for he was always gay and, like his father, filled with animation and a kind of jocose merriment. He loved to sing and dance, to play the trombone and, most of all it seemed to us, to tease. He looked like Pan, the god of shepherds, especially when he played his musical instrument, for his nose was long and thin above it, his eyes crinkled with laughter and his ears pointed upward into his brown, curly hair.

Whereas the war had matured Demosthenes and deepened his religious bent, Achilles came home gayer than ever, singing "Mademoiselle from Armentières" (considerably watered down for our childish ears) and "How're You Gonna Keep 'Em Down on the Farm?"

One of the things he loved to tease us about was the parrot. Auntie called it Sibyl of Cumae because pollies have a long life and the Sibyl lived to be a thousand years old. But there was more to it than that, and this is the story, according to Greek mythology:

Apollo gave the gift of prophecy to the Sibyl of Cumae. But, infuriated when she refused to become his mistress, he took a terrible revenge. One day she took a handful of sand and begged him to grant her a year of life for each grain she held. Apollo, realizing she had neglected to ask for continuing youth, granted her wish, and she grew so old and shriveled that she was kept in a cage. There, screaming out her prophecies, she became wrinkled and dark and no bigger than a Greek black olive, and when the boys passing by shouted to her in her cage, "Sibyl, what do you want?" she used to answer, "I want to die."

The parrot did not shriek prophecies, but through long and arduous summers we had taught it to half sing, half screech a few bars from "Farmer in the Dell." When Achilles returned from overseas, where he had learned to speak a little French, he at once set about teaching this meager knowledge to the polly. The result was that the bird learned to croak *"Qu'est que c'est que ça?"* It also screamed *"Allo, allo, entrez!"* whenever anyone knocked at the door, and *"Au revoire! Au revoire!"* when they left. We were aggravated no end every time we went up to the cage and, in our usual trio, began to chant "Farmer in the Dell" only to have Achilles rap smartly against the wall so that the poor, confused bird would respond by garbling French and English together and uttering such an absurdity as, "*Allo, allo,* farmer in the dell, *qu'est que c'est que ça?*"

When Auntie discovered the parrot could speak French, she was overcome by a desire to teach it Greek and tried tirelessly to get it to say *khali maris* which means good morning, but with no favorable result. I think the poor bird was too bewildered by this time to progress further as a linguist, and, as a matter of fact, as time went by it settled down to saying nothing more than "*Qu'est que c'est que ça?*"—which, after all, was perhaps a good question.

Much of our time was spent in plotting tricks to play on Achilles to pay him back for his endless teasing. But most of all we wished to catch him by the heel, for he insisted, like the great warrior Achilles, whose mother anointed him with ambrosia and dipped him in the river Styx to make him invulnerable, that he, too, was impregnable except in the heel by which he had been held.

He often allowed us to pound with our fists on his chest, neck, arms and head to prove this point, but never, in any circumstance, would he allow us to touch his heel. We made a great point of catching him unawares and striking him at this allegedly vulnerable point, but he was ever watchful in our presence and made a great to-do about hurrying to put his shoes on or racing into the bathroom to lock the door should we come upon him in the process of dressing.

We made many intricate and involved plans to catch

him in the middle of the night and lay upon his naked heel with violence in an attempt to prove, once and for all, that his was just a plain, old heel like anybody else's plain, old heel. But circumstances always interfered with our plans.

Achilles' favorite tune on the trombone was "Wabash Blues," while his brother, Demosthenes, who played the piccolo, loved "Clair de Lune." As they often practiced at the same time, each refusing to give up a chosen hour to the other, there was usually much argument and slamming of doors all over the house on these occasions, for the blare of one instrument against the high, shrill sound of the other was nerve-racking.

I think it was a kind of *outrance* between them, a single-minded, inflexible determination not to give up their individual identities, which was exemplified by the different instruments they played. With an almost passionate willfulness they would play on and on at the same time until Auntie, holding her head, would cry, *"Thawxa see aw Theos!"* which means "Glory be to God!" and go upstairs to put an end to it.

But one day Achilles stopped suddenly and of his own accord, in the midst of his practicing, and we heard only the high, sweet strains of "Clair de Lune" floating through the house. It seemed, in a way, a lonely sound, for the silence from Achilles' room was unprecedented and seemed to indicate resignation and defeat.

Later, when Auntie went upstairs to investigate, she found Achilles gargling mouthwash, and his face was hot and flushed. A few days later he lay in his bed suffering from pneumonia. The whole house was subdued as the doctor came and went, and Demosthenes put his piccolo away and hovered, ever watchful, by his brother's bed.

The anxious mood of the household soon transferred itself to us, and we were sure Achilles would die. We spoke of this solemnly among ourselves, for we knew he was not really invulnerable, and we attempted, in our grave consultations, to imagine life without him.

We remembered his laughter and his teasing with a kind of reverence, even spoke with veneration of the time he gave us soap sandwiches. The times he put pepper on our ice cream, gum in our shoes and a frog in the bureau drawer were our dearest and most treasured memories. We were grieved beyond measure at our own shortcomings and failings where he was concerned, and longed for but a single opportunity to expiate our sins.

No matter how often Auntie would tell us that we had nothing to fear and that our cousin was making daily progress, we refused to relinquish this new and overwhelming experience in sorrow. No one had to tell us to be quiet, for we spent our time in the most sober and subdued activities, lingering near the house and scanning each face for signs of sudden grief. A kind of loneliness descended upon us and, when a dog howled one night, we took it as a certain sign that Achilles' hour was near.

Despite our pessimistic outlook, however, the day finally came when Auntie told us that our cousin was well enough to see us and we might go up to his room for a visit. But when we entered, he had fallen off to sleep and, in his restlessness, had turned over on his stomach, rumpling the sheets so that both feet were exposed.

Then, so great was our love, so chastened by sorrow were we, so unwilling to leave any stone unturned that might bring him safely back to us, that none of us said a word as Pericles went silently forward and gently laid a handkerchief over Achilles' naked heels.

Thea and the Dirty Yellow Dog

OF ALL the people who lived in the octagonal house, none attempted to hold the reins of our destiny in her hands more resolutely than Thea. And, I may add, with less favorable result. Tirelessly she wielded, molded, guided, lectured, washed, scrubbed, harangued and fought to bring us to terms with life, but in spite of it all we were never quite able to grasp anything particularly beneficial from her teachings.

Her real name was Sophie Martin and she had been engaged first as a companion to my aunt, when she was a bride, and had stayed on as governess to my cousins when they were children. Now she remained as a member of the family, although a rather anomalous one, I must say. Her staunch Southern background, her American ways and her intolerance of anything relating to foreign culture gave her a rather parenthetical quality, as if her place in the family were firm but isolated.

We called her Thea, which means aunt in Greek, and were fascinated by her clothes. She never changed the style of her dress from the day she appeared until the day she died. She always wore little black high-button shoes, a long, full-skirted dress (either black or white) and a quaint little cap.

She had round, black eyes, bright and shiny as shoe buttons, a turned-up nose and a mouth like a slot in a mailbox. Her white hair was drawn into a knot on top of her head. She had a shape like an egg timer, and she was a constitutional kill-joy. As long as I knew Thea she was an old lady, crippled by rheumatism and a finished attitude about life, which she claimed had treated her badly all the way round.

One of the things that life had done to her was to allow the South to lose the War Between The States. She often referred to General Grant, who had defeated her idol, Lee, as a blackguard and a coward. She would claim that, drunk and staggering at his post, beseeched by his lieutenants to let his war-weary soldiers rest, Grant would answer by flinging his hand toward the battlefield and crying, "Thr-r-row them in!"

She charged that in his private life he was weak, immoral and alcoholic, having to rely on his horse to guide him home after an evening of debauchery. So entrenched was she in her hatred of the North, so bitter in the defeat of the South, that although she was a small woman seventy-five years old, she would rise to her feet during these diatribes and grow tall with fury. Let a discussion arise about Alexander the Great, however, and she simply sat tatting and humming, indifferent to the exigencies of Greece and Persia.

Auntie regarded her with suspicion and sometimes with apprehension. Her American opinions were disturbing and constituted a threat to Auntie's little stronghold of Greek culture thriving on the outskirts of a great American city. But a saving grace was that Thea was a Southerner and, like most Southerners, she relied strongly on the gentilities of the past. Gallantry, courtesy, delicacy, these were standards by which ladies and gentlemen were measured, and Auntie was able to ignore some of Thea's more caustic remarks inasmuch as she upheld so agreeable a pattern of behavior.

I do not know why, but we liked her and somehow understood her, although she was bitter, hardhearted and almost always rather unpleasant. For some reason I was her special pet, and she allowed me certain privileges which at times had the effect of setting my sister and brother against me. For one thing, I was allowed to sit next to her at table and eat all the icing off her cake. For another, she curled my hair every day, making long, sausagelike convolutions and setting the whole off with an enormous butterfly bow of watered-silk ribbon. And she took me into her confidence, telling me how cruelly life had treated her and how little one could expect from those to whom one had been kind. Sometimes, rocking and tatting away in her room on the third floor, she would describe for me the bleakness of her past, the desert quality of her future, while I, sitting close by with my doll, would regard her with wide-eyed wonder and a kind of uncertain pity.

"The more you do for people, the more you get it in the neck," she would say, her fingers working automatically with hook and shuttle as she rocked back and forth. But if I voiced so much as a small complaint of my own, she would fix me with a level eye and adjure me to count my blessings. "May you never have less" was a favorite saying of hers, implying that she herself had known what it was to hit rock bottom.

This acid outlook on life was, of course, the result of her marriage to the Dirty Yellow Dog. We all knew about him: the villain in her past, a man who courted her with flowery phrases and fancy ways, married her for her savings and then, with a curl of his lip and a twist of his mustache, left her for another woman. She referred to him only as the Dirty Yellow Dog, and though we would beseech her by the hour to tell us his name, she would refuse, declaring she would rather voice an oath than repeat it.

This fascinated us as well as one other thing about her—her secret bed. Although we spent much time in her room having tea, which she brewed for us on a little gas plate, we could never understand where she slept.

Compared with the rest of the house, which was lavishly furnished with beaded lamps, enormous chandeliers and the ornate furniture of the period, Thea's room was marked by a nunlike austerity. This was in

accordance with her nature, which recognized no fol-
derol. Stiff and severe, it contained a chair, a table, a
high chest of drawers and a bureau—but no bed.

Thea would not give up the secret, and it was a
constant guessing game each afternoon when, at four
o'clock, she would blow a little whistle at her window and we would come scampering from wherever
we were, in the orchard, under the mulberry tree
or in the barn, to her room for our afternoon tea.
Mama later decided that tea made children nervous
and put a stop to this small pleasure, but while it
lasted it was a great occasion for guessing the where-
abouts of the bed.

One afternoon when Thea went to town to visit her
only living relatives, two nieces who had treated her
with "nothing but ingratitude," we decided to go up
to her room and have a look around for the bed.

Opening closets, looking for trap doors, fumbling for
sliding panels, we eventually discovered that the high
chest of drawers swung around and concealed a folding
bed which pulled down into the room. This was a
marvelous revelation, indeed, and we were so elated
we decided to look for other secrets as well. Opening
one of the drawers, we came upon the greatest secret
of all—a folded paper clearly marked MARRIAGE
LICENSE and embellished with a drawing of two
clasped hands and a dove. Now at last we could dis-
cover the name of the Dirty Yellow Dog!

In the drawer were other things whose significance
escaped our childish hearts but which nevertheless remain to haunt me today. In a box we found her wed-

ding slippers, yellowing kid with little pointed toes and rosettes of satin, a pair of long, kid gloves, a dried bouquet of flowers, and, among all these things, a card which said, in fine Spencerian writing, *Dearest Heart, I love you.*

To these things, then, she had clung through all the long bitter years. Wrapped in tissue paper and laid away, they were the faded mementos of a lost love, as hidden and secret as her heart, concealed so long beneath a rigid and uncompromising bosom.

Their heartbreak was lost on us, however. With anxious hands we unfolded the paper to learn, at last, the mysterious name of the Dirty Yellow Dog—only to find, to our chagrin, that she had taken a sharp instrument and cut it out in its entirety, leaving only her own name in its single, lonely propriety.

Mine Host

As I look back on the lovely, lost days at Parnassus, they all seem edged with gold, as if sunlight and magic touched them in a special way. This was partly because the whole place contained an atmosphere at once elegant and provincial, partly because the people who lived there sustained this same strange juxtaposition of formality with an easy, even carefree indulgence. With nectar and honey they filled our days, while they made sure the cup from which we drank was most properly and prudently made. Thus while it was perfectly all right for children to slide down the bannisters, one always said, "Excuse me," if one hurtling body crashed into another hurtling body. And while it was considered acceptable to say "*Ach Theo Mu!*" which means "Oh, my God!" in Greek, it was unheard of to utter such vulgarities as "Darn it!" "Shut up!" or "Hot dog!" in English.

Likewise, when Aphrodite fled to her room in tears, either because she was not allowed to study medicine or not allowed to marry an American, we were expected to remove ourselves both physically and spiritually from the issue. Such disputes were not considered favorable to the emotional adjustment of children. All the same we sometimes listened.

"You are Greek and you will be happiest married to a Greek," Auntie would say and she clung to this mandatory doctrine though cousin Aphrodite wept and wailed.

One time I heard one of Mama's brothers—my Uncle John who was very Americanized and all on the side of Free Selection—tell Auntie that the trouble with her was that she just happened to get a lucky break. When I asked Mama what he meant she first gave me a lecture on not using slang expressions such as "lucky break" and then told me how Auntie and Uncle Demetrius happened to get married.

They met in Chicago, where my grandfather, a priest, had been sent from Athens to found the Greek Orthodox church. His daughters, Elene, Eurydice and Penelope (Mama) and his two sons, John and Themistocles, were all who survived of his twelve children.

Elene was a beautiful young girl, pure in heart and body, and she came of good family and had had a stern religious training. For these reasons she was greatly sought after by the young Greek men of the community whose parents desired they marry into their own religion and nationality. And the fact that Elene had a delicate face like a cameo, with straight, even features, luminous amber eyes, curling brown hair and a figure as slender and graceful as a goddess, made her a pearl beyond price. In her seventeenth year she received four hundred proposals which, in short, was a proposal from every eligible young man in the Greek community. My grandfather refused them all—this being his province—for it was his intention that this beautiful young virgin should make a marriage which would insure her a future both sound and pious.

Such a man appeared in the person of Demetrius Jannopoulo, the Greek consul from St. Louis, who had come to Chicago to importune grandfather to found a Greek Orthodox church in his city.

He was nearly thirty years older than Elene, a dark and dashing gentleman who owned a tent and awning company—a man of wealth and position and devout religious faith. Grandfather knew that King George had conferred upon him the Order of the Royal Cross, which was the most distinguished decoration of the Greek nation, one which carried with it privileges and exemptions which exceeded those granted the nobility. Allowing for just a touch of snobbishness, even in a holy man, and considering the true worth of my uncle as well, Grandfather highly approved this match, and despite the difference in their ages, Demetrius loved and wooed and won Elene, giving her for her wedding present his beautiful home, Parnassus, and a pair of fabulous diamond earrings.

"Your auntie truly loved Demetrius, though he was

her father's choice," said Mama. "She was very fortunate and that is what your Uncle John meant when he happened to let slip a slangy phrase which I do not want to hear any of you ever repeat." Then, in order not to place my uncle at a disadvantage (for Mama was extremely loyal to every member of her family), she added: "I am sure your uncle heard some common ruffians use the expression and thought it was funny."

Grandfather himself officiated at their wedding. The year was 1892. Demetrius and his bride were guests at a ball given in Chicago for Their Royal Highnesses, the Infanta Eulalie and the Infante Antonia of Spain. When they returned from their honeymoon to St. Louis, the papers made many references to "The Fair Helen" and reported her "a bride worthy to be worshipped in such a temple."

I wish I could have seen Elene, standing tall, beautiful and pristine in her little gray traveling suit with its mink muff and her tiny hat trimmed with violets as she viewed for the first time her new home.

It was built in the form of a Greek cross, the four arms of which were enclosed in an octagonal shape. Each arm extended from a huge center hall which followed the outer form of the house so that it, too, was octagonal in shape, the very heart of the house. Standing in its center, Elene could look four stories high to a cupola from which hung a most magnificent chandelier, its glass globes and beads and glittering prisms bursting forth like resplendent fountains at intervals of each story.

Every floor was surrounded by an interior balcony,

from the lower one of which hung an ornate bronze fringe made of chains which were strung with colored balls and golden acorns. Erected on the newel posts of the wide staircase carpeted in red, two tall bronze Greek figures of night and day held aloft electrified torches. On all sides the elaborately furnished rooms opened wide and graciously to receive her.

Did her eyes shine with pleasure, as I have always known them to do when she was proud or happy? Or did she cast them down, modest and a little frightened, the daughter of a simple Greek priest?

I do not know. By the time I was born my aunt was long used to Parnassus. She was then in her forties and moved among its many rooms, lovely, gracious, sweet and good. And if, at times, she disclosed an iron hand in a velvet glove, it was only in her determination to preserve a culture purely Hellenic in her home. For she was as Greek as the first stone Pyrrha threw behind her from which, according to mythology, sprang the Hellenic race. Because of this, she was not only sometimes at odds with her children but also occasionally found herself rather far afield with Uncle Demetrius, who earnestly attempted to blend Greek culture with an American flavor.

As long as I knew my uncle, he looked exactly like the Kaiser Wilhelm of Germany, for his hair had turned white by the time we were born. He was short in stature, had a pointed white beard and waxed mustaches, a rather large nose and eyes as bright and glinting as two blue diamonds. His skin was ruddy and he was as agile and tireless as a boy of sixteen.

Until he was nearly eighty years old he climbed trees, vaulted fences and ran and shouted as if he were in the very pink of his youth.

One day when Artemis, Pericles and I were pursuing the thankless chore of digging to China in the arbor, I looked up to see Auntie and Uncle Demetrius strolling hand in hand across the lawn. Suddenly he vaulted over a wall, climbed up a tree and plucked a magnolia which he returned to pin in her hair. Then, putting his arm around her waist, he kissed her on the cheek.

I watched this little tableau with mild interest, then turned to my sister and brother.

"Just think," I observed, dropping my shovel to point a thumb across the lawn, "Grandfather might have picked out a husband that couldn't even climb a tree." As Artemis and Pericles slowly digested this, I went back to work, adding: "She sure got a lucky break. . . ."

Grandfather

Uncle Demetrius was, of course, the head of his house. This was never disputed although, by some simple recognition of theological priority, it was commonly understood that Grandfather was a cut above him.

Thus, although we might conceivably neglect to greet our uncle from time to time, or in our enthusiasm for a game toss him a negligible hello, when Grandfather entered a room we, as children, were brought up to go forward and kiss his hand. And, although he spoke English haltingly, we were expected to spend a little time in respectful conversation with him. He asked how we were, and we replied that we were well, thank you, thus exhausting our knowledge of conversational Greek. He would then stroke our heads, say something we did not understand and finally indicate that we could go. His smile was sweet and benign, and his manner so gentle and kind, that, although we often did not understand what he was saying, we knew it was the language of love.

He was usually a little removed from the family, spending most of his time in his room studying, reading the Bible or writing a history of religions. He was a scholar as well as a minister, a man of great knowledge, an authority on history and philosophy. Although he spoke eight languages fluently, his English was poor, and thus Mama's determination to have him teach us Greek came to naught. For Grandfather, in attempting to translate, often translated into French, Italian or Russian.

Being old and wise, he spoke little, sometimes sitting for hours in silence, his hands clasped across his middle, his lips forming an enigmatic expression, his eyes veiled in a faraway mist.

His name was Panagiotis Phiambolis, and he was born in 1840 in Ithaca, one of the islands of Greece. There was always about him a kind of meditative introspection, and he had a fine and beautiful and somehow ancient face, like a Rembrandt painting. His eyes were deep-set under rounded lids, his nose thin and aquiline, curved and arched like a high-prancing stallion, and he had long, white hair, which fell to his shoulders in the manner of his faith, and a long, white beard.

There was something noble in his face, a nobility not of pride but of wisdom and gentility and inner grace. The ancient Greek thinker divided the things of life into two parts, the temporal and the eternal, and was interested only in the eternal, which he spoke of as excellence. Grandfather had this quality of excellence. There was also something indomitable about him, a kind of purpose and meaning to his life which gave him a certain power. In his youth he had been a big man of formidable strength, and even in his aging years he was neither stooped nor bent, although he always walked with a cane.

I do not know what Grandfather thought about in the hours he sat with the veiled expression in his eyes, but I always thought it was of his son, Themistocles.

Mama, in speaking of Grandfather's great kindness and gentleness of manner, told us a story about him which had the purpose of being a lesson in ethics. She said that when he lived in Chicago with his family, his son, Themistocles, had come to ask his permission to go sailing on Lake Michigan. Grandfather refused, it being Sunday, a day of rest and service to God. One word led to another, and they argued bitterly, for Themistocles was nineteen years old, of a wild and fiery disposition and a great trial to his father. When he announced he would go sailing despite his father's wishes, Grandfather was infuriated. In anger he raised his cane to strike his son and, in so doing, struck his hand against a table instead and injured his little finger, which remained crooked at the end forever after.

Themistocles fled from the house straight to Lake Michigan where, in furious denial of his father's authority, he went sailing with his friends. Then, as if

God's wrath had struck, a sudden squall blew up, the skies grew dark, the wind whipped across the lake, the boat was overturned and Themistocles was drowned.

Grandfather, heartbroken, took this as a sign from God, not that Themistocles had sinned, but that he, his father, had done so in attempting to strike his son. The boy's death was his punishment, and the crooked finger an everlasting reminder to hold his temper.

Soon after, he had another son and named him Themistocles for his departed boy. This was Mama's youngest brother, my uncle who played the piano and was of so mild and sweet a disposition.

On Sundays Grandfather officiated at the Greek Orthodox Church. On these occasions he attained a kind of magnificence in our eyes, for he was always attired in long, colored robes made of stiff silk embroidered with gold thread. Around his neck there hung a heavy, jeweled cross, and in his hand he held an incense burner, ornately worked in gold, which he swung by three bronze chains. On his head he wore a high, satin hat, curved in front and embroidered with gold.

The whole church smelled of incense and candle wax and flowers. From time to time the choir would sing in a queer, minor, quavering chant, echoing the words of Byzantine music—a high, nasal, grievous intonation that sustained a note of anguish. In the midst of lighted candles, against a backdrop of a huge crucifix inscribed with the letters INRI, Grandfather would raise his hand in benediction over the bowed heads of the congregation and murmur, in a kind of mystic monotone, the words of the Lord's Prayer in Greek.

The service was long and, for us, arduous, as it involved much standing and kneeling, but we accepted it all with a mild reverence. However, by the time Grandfather got around to the sermon we were glad to sit down and know we could so remain for a while.

Then, as Grandfather began to speak, the church would be filled with listening silence, broken only occasionally by a cough, a baby's squall or hurrying footsteps down the aisle as someone took an irascible child outside. After a while the closeness of the room, the smell of incense, the hypnotic glow of the candles and the seemingly endless monotone of Grandfather's voice using words we did not understand would cause us to stir restlessly in our pew, and we would whisper to Mama that we did not feel well. This never failed to result in our instant removal to a small, enclosed yard behind the church, where we were allowed to play until the service was over. Mama always looked at us, however, as if she did not quite go along with the validity of our sudden illness.

Two or three times a year Grandfather would bless the house. On these occasions the family would gather together and follow him from room to room, standing with bowed heads and making the sign of the cross as he swung the incense burner from side to side, supplicating the Lord, in His divine mercy, to bring peace, love and prosperity to this house. Always afterward, for a whole day, a kind of benevolence seemed to fall over the household, and there would not be a cross word spoken. Even the subject of whether or not

Aphrodite would be allowed to study medicine was somehow held in abeyance, for this was a topic of dispute which invariably caused much argument, tears and slamming of doors all over the house.

Aphrodite longed to be a doctor. Auntie considered the profession unseemly for a young girl and refused to give her consent. Uncle Demetrius, on the other hand, was at least willing to take it under advisement. At last it was decided to ask Grandfather's opinion.

When the subject was taken before him, Grandfather pondered it for many days and came to a conclusion: woman is so constituted that the profession of medicine, or any other profession, would result in a certain sacrifice to her natural proclivities. This settled the matter as far as everyone in the family was concerned, except Aphrodite. She argued, pleaded, wept to no avail.

Besides Grandfather's opinion on this subject, I found that he had also another opinion regarding women. One day when I was about eight years old, I was sorting through some pictures of movie stars I had collected. One was of Blanche Sweet. I was looking at it, admiring her lovely, golden hair, her sloping shoulders coyly veiled in tulle and her angelic expression, when Grandfather appeared. Tapping my shoulder with his cane, he held out his hand to see the picture.

I was a little embarrassed, thinking the picture too nude and too theatrical for the eyes of such a holy man, when he handed it to Mama who was sitting near by, with the following remark and a bored shrug: "*Axinos ke analatos.*"

When he left, I asked Mama what he had said, and she laughed and told me Grandfather did not think much of Blanche Sweet and had called her "Unsalted and unvinegared," an expression which means "Blah."

En Famille

THE Greek cross, which formed the main body of the house, comprised four rooms on the first floor, each of which opened off the octagonal reception hall. The angles between consisted of pantry, porches, stairway and fireplace.

One arm of the cross was the Billiard Room-library and contained a large bird's-eye maple table inlaid with ivory and covered with green felt. Here the family played pocket billiards, selecting their cues and chalk from a glass-enclosed cabinet, and keeping score by pushing little markers, which were strung on a wire stretched high across the room.

The ladies were always rather jaunty when they played this game, cocking their heads and closing one eye as they cued the ball, attempting, in some vague

discussion arose and a point was in dispute, there was an immediate and speedy exodus to the Billiard Room to thumb frantically through one of these volumes for proof. I do not know by what means a whole family acquires a passion for knowledge, for music, for the arts, for nature—but such was the case in this household. Not one member of the family had any desire to remain idle, and when they were not pursuing their studies, their work or their games, when they were not gaily dancing the quadrille together or dressing up in costumes (a favorite pastime), they simply gathered round the table in the dining room, there hotly to debate any given subject from politics to polygamy.

The octagonal reception hall was a room in itself, a kind of family gathering place, somewhat akin to a hotel lobby. There were enormous standing lamps of bronze, couches and chairs covered with plum-colored frieze and an octagonal-shaped inlaid table, which stood in the center of the hall under the enormous chandelier which hung from the cupola. There was a fireplace and a burled-walnut grand piano on which stood a glass dome encasing a heron which Uncle Demetrius had shot. (Our uncle was a very good shot and proud of it. One night he became so annoyed by the hooting of an owl perched atop the arbor that he made short shrift of the bird. Rising from his bed, as he had threatened for a week to do, he went to the window in his nightcap and shirt and, in the darkness, drew a bead on the poor thing with his pistol and shot it dead—not, however, before he woke us all up to see him perform this act of skill.) The heron was a beautiful bluish-green color and stood tirelessly on one leg under the glass dome.

Besides the dead crane, the live parrot had his cage in the hall, and there was a victrola and cabinet for music.

We loved the reception hall, for in the summertime it was always dim and cool, and we liked to walk in our bare feet on the inlaid Greek key design that made a border around the parquet floor. In the winter, during holidays, its soft lights and the roaring fire filled our hearts with warmth and that wonderful feeling of safety, so dear to children though their lives be sheltered and their worlds secure.

There were other rooms in the house which were special and meaningful to us, but I think this reception hall, which seemed by its very architecture and construction to be the heart of the house, was the one we loved most dearly.

One of the nicest things about it was that when we sat here, drawing or coloring or looking at pictures in a book, we could be an inconspicuous part of any family gathering. We had long since learned that if we sat quietly, occupied with our own affairs, the grownups often forgot us. If they were singing or playing the piano, as they sometimes did in the evenings, or if they were having a game of billiards, or if they were gathered round the dining-room table, drinking coffee and having a *megalophonia,* we could see and hear it all.

Megalophonia simply means soundness in Greek, and is a word employed to mean a heated dispute.

Megalophonias arise out of nowhere, turn into vehement discussions and mean nothing. They are simply a part of the passionate nature of the Greeks, who are a demonstrative people, as emotional in argument as they are in love. Their responses are all impressive, whether it be burning anger, profound pity, rapturous love or heated disagreement. In conversation they often use their hands and their hearts, and they are constitutionally incapable of the Anglo-Saxon's dispassionate and self-contained objectivity. To a Greek it is a strange and unhealthy symptom not to Feel Deeply, and they have an expression for people of calm disposition. They call them *Nero vrasto,* which means boiled water.

The dining room was directly across the hall from the Billiard Room—the opposite arm of the cross. The walls were covered in olive-green burlap over a dado of green leather. At one end there was a corner cabinet with red glass doors. At the other was a china cabinet which contained a hand-painted fish set, elaborately displayed, and out of which all the fishes' eyes stared dolefully. The table was fifteen feet long, always covered with a white tablecloth and set with silver candlesticks, a three-tiered silver epergne filled with flowers, two cruet sets and two cut-glass tumblers filled with teaspoons. On the sideboard there was a decanter of wine and a silver pitcher filled with ice water, which was always frosty and wet on the outside.

There were never less than eight, often as many as twenty and sometimes even thirty people for meals. Auntie sat at one end of the table, Thea at the other, while Uncle Demetrius and Grandfather sat in the center at opposite sides. All the meals were grandiloquent and hearty affairs, but I particularly remember breakfasts prepared by an enormous German cook. There were halved cantaloupes served on ice, along with broiled mackerel, fried zucchini squash, homemade hard rolls, liver and brains and platters of fried eggs. And I cannot say why, or how it came to be, but one could eat breakfast at any time one arose —it was always ready, always hot, always pleasantly served. There was never any set hour for breakfast, although at dinner everyone came promptly to the table when the bell rang.

On week ends when Mama and Papa came out, as well as Aunt Eurydice and her husband, Uncle Alec, along with Uncle John and Uncle Themistocles and other relatives and friends, the table looked as if it were set for a banquet; yet it was only a family gathering, an ordinary meal and nothing more.

The other two arms of the cross consisted of the kitchen wing and the parlor. The parlor walls were covered in rose-colored burlap, and on the floor was a pink Oriental rug. Everything in this room was rather fragile. Dresden figurines pirouetted on the mantle and tended their sheep, the chairs were each covered in a different colored velvet—rose, blue, green, amethyst and gold—and on a gold table in front of the window there was a potted fern. On another table was a red-velvet family album, and lace curtains hung at the windows. This was our least favorite room in all the house, for while it was very pretty, the family

never gathered here. I always thought of it as a skinny
lady without a lap.

But best of all we liked the big octagonal reception
hall where, on week ends, Papa led the quadrille.
Sometimes the entire family would dress in costume
and Papa would wear a fustanella, an accordion-
pleated, short skirt which was the uniform of the
Greek guardsmen. Mama and Auntie would wear
their chitons, Aphrodite would wrap herself in silk or
satin or red crepe paper, in the manner of an Egyptian
or Indian princess, Achilles, Demosthenes and Aristotle would array themselves as Greek gods or American generals, according to their mood, and Artemis,
Pericles and I would be given costumes left over from
our cousins' childhood.

In this garb everyone would merrily dance the
quadrille, tripping back and forth, holding arms high
to catch one another's hands as Papa called out the
steps. It was a kind of square dance, very fast and
intricate and breath-taking, and we children merely
ran around in a kind of jumbled nonsense, which no
one seemed to mind, as the victrola whizzed away to
tunes from *The Red Mill.*

No one ever seemed to find children in the way in
this wonderful house. We ran around the hall and
held up our hands and twirled until we were dizzy
in the most delightful freedom. Now and again a
grownup would catch us and spin us around and then
let us go as they madly went their way.

Afterward, still in costume, they would gather round
the piano and sing and play the guitar, and the house

would be filled with their voices in laughter and song. Thea always seemed to enjoy the music from *The Red Mill* or songs like "Flow Gently Sweet Afton" or "Rocked In The Cradle Of The Deep." But when they began to sing Greek folk songs, as they invariably did, she would make her mouth tight and heave her rheumatic body up the steps, one at a time, clutching the banister as she mumbled, "Foreigners!" under her breath. In this way she made her journey up to her room, where, no doubt, she nurtured her bile with a volume called *Under The Heel Of Grant*, which she kept by her bedside.

One night Thea was about to make her usual exit when Uncle John held out his hand. He was a very witty man, filled with subtle humor and a love of fun. He was Mama's brother and looked very much like her with his dreamy eyes, his dark hair and his olive skin. Bantering Thea a little, for her tirades amused him, he asked, "Where are you going, Thea? Why don't you stick around and join the fun?"

Thea stood stock still and gave him her level, Southern gaze.

"Suh," said she, eyes flashing, "I will thank you to keep your impudent hands to yourself. I was not brought up to make a fool of myself, and I do not intend, at the age of seventy-five, to begin by singing such garbled tomfoolery." She drew herself as straight and tall as possible and fixed him with a fiery eye. "And I will tell you this. If it were not for your General Grant, that jackass, drunken coward who ground the Confederate soldier under his damnyankee heel, there would still be a place for me in a land where ladies and gentlemen conduct themselves in a genteel manner and do not cavort around like dern fools."

With this she turned on her heel and began her arduous assent up the stairs while Uncle John, who was a lawyer, shrugged his broad shoulders, spread his hands wide and said, *"Tee na su kama."*

The most appropriate translation for this idiom in English would be "Sue me."

The True Sign of Love

PAPA was the handsomest man in St. Louis. Mama always said so, and invariably added, "And he is as good as gold." In later years she added yet another tribute, proudly acclaiming him the best-dressed man in St. Louis. I believe Papa was so elected by some women's organization, and Mama was as proud as a peacock.

Papa was, indeed, an unusually handsome man. He was tall and thin with dark, wavy hair, sparkling brown eyes and silken mustaches through which his white teeth glistened when he smiled, as even and perfect as pearls. His nose was straight and strong, his chin firm with a slight cleft, and he had a sweet and mobile mouth.

There was always about him a certain elegance. He was immaculate in his dress and smelled faintly of eau de Cologne, cigars and Lavoris mouthwash. He wore sideburns, a dark, ruby ring on his finger, a stickpin in his cravat, and whenever he went out he wore spats and carried a cane. Despite the attention he gave to material things (he had a collection of five hundred neckties) and his love of fun, he was a thoughtful man, a student of philosophy and a devotee of the arts.

Sometimes in St. Louis, if Mama were indisposed, he would take me to the symphony on a Saturday night. There, in top hat and tails and an Inverness cape, Papa would enter the lobby from the street with me beside him. He was instantly the focal point of every woman's gaze, for his striking good looks caused a mild commotion wherever he went. At these times I stood as tall as possible and clung to Papa's hand while he, looking rather haughty and detached, would light a gold-tipped cigarette casually, gazing aloofly over the heads of the twittering ladies.

In all truth I believe this proud and disdainful air was not so much vanity on Papa's part as an embarrassed reluctance to find himself the center of so much female ogling. I presume that, being good as gold, he felt a certain moral obligation to ignore the frank invitation he found in other women's eyes when he was not with Mama, but at the same time I must admit he always dressed to the hilt to assure himself of it.

When we were away at Parnassus for the summer, we always looked forward to Papa's week-end visits, for we were charmed by his presence, although there

was always a touch of formality in our relationship with him. He was Papa, and we were not expected to clamor over him, but to come and sit on his knee when invited.

Then he would tell us wonderful stories, which kept us enthralled, or do magic tricks with pennies or make shadows of animals on the wall with his hands. It would not have occurred to us to whoop and holler with him. And pillow fights were not in his line. Papa was not that kind of man. He was much too eminent, in our opinion, too consanguine for familiarity, and this feeling of respect for our parents was an essential part of our upbringing. No matter how gay he might be in family groups nor how often he might dress up in costume and lead the quadrille, he was nevertheless Papa, and this implied a sort of grandeur.

When we were still young children, Uncle Demetrius gave up the consulship, feeling he was growing too old for the post, and the Greek government appointed Papa to take his place. This was a very great honor, and when Papa wore his uniform, he looked like a dashing, romantic Broadway star done up for a musical. The uniform was made of black broadcloth, lavishly trimmed with silver braid. The long, narrow trousers, immaculately tailored coat with silver buttons' bearing the consulate crest (a Greek cross on a shield), the high silver-braided collar and the silver and black hat were all specially made to order for him, and he wore them with great elegance and dash. To complete the picture, a long sword hung from his side, encased in an ornate, silver sheath upon which Papa always rested one hand casually in a manner suggesting he might be awfully quick on the trigger. In this uniform there could be no doubt that Papa was indeed the handsomest man in St. Louis.

Papa did not look or behave like any other fathers we knew, especially those of our American friends. These were all shadowy figures, half-hidden behind newspapers, or jolly, rather rough-and-tumble men, who wrestled with their sons and mussed their daughters' hair. But we thought him the most wonderful father in the world, as handsome and good as Mama proclaimed him to be.

One thing we knew about Papa was that he loved Mama very much. Whenever they were together they held hands, kissed secretly and called each other Dearest. Mama, more tempestuous by nature than Papa, sometimes made issues of small matters over which she felt deeply, and when Papa refused to rise to the occasion, her impatience would grow by leaps and bounds until it reached magnificent proportions of Latin vehemence. Then she would not call him Dearest but would always address him by his full name, Hector Pasmezoglu. Whenever Mama called Papa Hector Pasmezoglu, we knew things were popping. Afterward she would always say, sadly, "I shouldn't have been so angry with him. He is as good as gold." And Papa would bring her a big box of Dolly Varden chocolates. The box had a picture of a lady on it, presumably Dolly herself, whose chin rested on the backs of her hands while her face, wreathed in a beatific expression, gazed out between loose waves of hair. Sometimes when Papa was feeling particularly affectionate, he called Mama Dolly Varden.

They adored each other, and their love was both impassioned and sweet. Mama was a lush plum, olive-skinned and curvaceous. She had large, limpid eyes, soft, black hair and beautiful teeth. Her arms were plump and round, her bosom full, her waist tiny. Everything about her was soft, beguiling and dulcet—except, of course, her temperament, which sometimes brought about scenes in which Mama could be very fiery and weep and toss her head and stamp her little foot. But Papa was like Mars, the god of war who, though not invincible, was always accompanied by victory. True to type, they always fell into each other's arms at length, and the reconciliation scene was both beautiful and grandiloquent.

Mama was a strange admixture of loving wife and mother, dutiful to a fault, and an ardent champion of women's rights. Actually, most of her expositions on The Vote, Birth Control, Bobbed Hair and Equality In Business took place in the bosom of the family, for Mama wished no more than to win the intellectual victory, and I cannot imagine her ever getting out in public and stumping for anything. When she was not championing something at the dinner table, she was busily living a very happy and prudent life.

One of the things she and Papa disagreed about was her singing. She had a magnificent voice and had been offered a contract to sing with the Metropolitan Opera in New York, but Papa put his foot down.

When a friend of Mama's, Helen Traubel, who used to visit in our home before the days of her great glory, made her bow at the Metropolitan, Mama said, "Now there's a woman I admire," and clapped madly in the thundering applause. It was supposed to make Papa feel apologetic, but it had no such effect.

He allowed her to sing with the St. Louis Symphony Orchestra, but he would not, on any account, let her accept money. When she insisted that every woman ought to Earn a Little Pin Money of Her Own, Papa said that was nonsense. He said that no Wife of His would go out and earn her living. Then Mama always said a woman should have Freedom to Come and Go. Papa said that no Wife of His would go gallivanting around the country living in hotels and leaving his babies in the care of servants while she accepted pay for a God-given talent.

Freedom to Come and Go and Pin Money were Mama's two intellectual goals for women, and when Papa, who gave her plenty of pin money as well as a nominal amount of freedom, challenged her on these subjects, she always answered darkly, "Women were not meant to be bound in chains, Hector Pasmezoglu."

As I sometimes overheard these arguments, which always ended in kisses and protestations of love but no solution, I would wait for the moment when Mama took her bow at the Odeon amidst wild applause. Then up the aisle would run ushers in uniform, bearing large baskets and bouquets of roses while Mama, holding as many as she could, would bow sweetly and acknowledge the compliment. She used to look so pretty, standing there in pale peach-colored pan velvet embroidered with passementerie and a floating scarf of chiffon around her shoulders, as she smiled and dropped her head. All the same I knew she was thinking that roses were not Pin Money.

Auntie did not like these discussions about careers for women, of which she did not approve. It was becoming more and more apparent that Mama was siding with Aphrodite in her desire to practice medicine, and, on top of this, Uncle Demetrius, a stickler for education, was joining forces with her. Lately he was finding the American way the best way, and his thinking was extremely progressive. Thus I would sometimes see Auntie's sweet face become rather porcelain, and when Mama veered off on one of her favorite family topics—a womans' right to wear rouge, to drive an automobile (sometimes she was even impetuous enough to include puffing a cigarette), to earn a living—Auntie would always try to change the subject. Then Mama would announce, as a final thrust, that she intended to have *her* daughters equip themselves for independence. (She was pretty good at her prognostications, too, for she was only a little off in selection. Although I turned out to be a writer, as Mama predicted, Artemis did not turn out to be a singer but a painter. However, we both grew up equipped to earn a little pin money now and then.)

For all this much ado about nothing (Mama would not have left Papa for so long as one night, much less have gone off to New York to have a career), our parents were, on the whole, sublimely happy together and exceedingly romantic and sentimental about each other. It was true that their love brought a certain comfort and security to us, but there were times when I doubted Papa truly loved me. If this emotion were to be indicated by demonstrativeness, as evidenced by Mama and Papa, then where, I wondered, did I fit in?

Papa, while affectionate, was rather spurious in his devotion, and Mama, recognizing this and attempting to make up for it, always painted a most wretched picture of our father working from dawn to dusk in a ceaseless effort to give us Everything. She also pictured him tossing and turning in his bed at night as he worried over our welfare. But I saw no indication of physical or emotional struggle in Papa. He was just very kind and affectionate in a temporary kind of way. It was all very well to tell stories and do magic tricks and even let us dance the quadrille with him—but where, I wondered, was the true sign of love?

Then one day I was seized and caught up in the epidemic of Spanish influenza that lay siege to the United States at the time of the First World War. It was a holiday and I was at Parnassus. I was put to bed with a high fever, and so contagious was the disease and so serious in its effects, that it was decided I should be taken back to St. Louis in an ambulance.

While I was deliriously looking forward to this unprecedented joy ride, the door to the spare room burst open and there was Papa. He was pale with anxiety and rushed to my bedside without taking off his hat, whereupon he sank to his knees and began stroking my hands. When I looked at him, two tears rolled down his cheeks and he was calling me his "darling little girl." Then he rose to his feet and cried angrily to Mama and Auntie, who were standing in the doorway, that if anything happened to me he would Sell Everything and go back to Greece.

Mama, who could go into a frenzy over a scratch— which she invariably referred to as a nasty wound— was taking my case of Spanish influenza quite calmly. Perhaps this was because she was always able to call upon some great inner strength in times of crisis, perhaps because she was to come down with the same disease in a day or two herself. In any case, she just smiled at Papa and said, I believe to tease him out of his panic, "Don't be silly, Dearest. You would never give up your five hundred neckties."

Then Papa said, "To *hell* with my neckties!" and fell to his knees again, enfolding me in his arms.

I was not feeling too badly, but I closed my eyes and tried to look as pale and close to death as possible, while I luxuriated in the warmth of his arms and the smell of cologne and cigars and Lavoris mouthwash.

Papa's profane and frightened outburst was, I knew at last, the true sign of love.

The Starving Armenians

DURING the First World War Mama asked Auntie and Uncle Demetrius if they would consider holding a Greek fete at Parnassus, the proceeds of which would go to the starving Armenians.

At that time there was a great campaign on to help these unfortunate victims of the war, and there were posters everywhere of little children, their bodies wracks of bones, their enormous, sunken eyes staring out of pinched faces beneath mops of uncombed hair. These were the starving Armenians, and they were always depicted holding out poor, thin, shrunken arms in a plea for help. Underneath the poster was a big caption which said: GIVE TILL IT HURTS. Even the most stonyhearted individual could not help being stirred by these wretched children, and Artemis, Pericles and I were moved to turning all our pennies over to donation boxes without a word of complaint. They were the most miserable pictures of children I have ever seen—starved, dirty, in rags, pitiful beyond compare—and no one could escape their hungry eyes as they stared out from every billboard, streetcar poster and corner sign.

Thea, who considered us overindulged, always held them up to us as examples of the truly wretched. "Think of the starving Armenians!" she would admonish, if we left so much as a bread crust on our plates, and she often informed us they would give anything for the very peach stones we threw away and would make a feast on the bones that were left on our plates. In due course, the starving Armenians became a kind of constant embarrassment to us, as it seems they would give anything for the soap that was left melting in the basin when we washed our hands, the sugar we spilled when Cousin Aphrodite taught us to make fudge, the milk we left standing on the porch to sour in the sun, the storybooks we scribbled in and tore. Thea was always there, making her mouth tight and evoking sorrowful images of freezing, hungry, homeless orphans who would give anything for the things we so carelessly squandered.

"May you never have less," she would say, no matter how unobtrusive we tried to be.

We were very glad, therefore, when Mama suggested the idea of a charity program, for she explained the money would help buy food and clothing for the starving Armenians, and we felt that with this aid they would no longer be in such dire straits, and the burden of our consciences would be lightened somewhat.

Auntie and Uncle Demetrius agreed at once, and plans were begun for a Greek fete to be given outdoors. Mama gathered together dancers and singers, musicians and orators, booths were installed where food and drinks were to be sold, and folding chairs were set up to accommodate a thousand people. Uncle Demetrius had programs printed and even composed a poem to be printed on the back which went like this:

Were I vested with the power of Apollo,
The god of the sun and the Muses,
I would ask the sun to shine on Parnassus,
Keeping the lawns ever green,
The flowers continually blooming.
And I would instruct the Muses
To fill the air with sweet melodies,
Thus wooing my guests
To linger within its gates.

Mama and Auntie worked like beavers to make the fete a success, arranging for costumes, music and the sale of tickets. Uncle Demetrius worried over his poem, writing and rewriting it, between times rushing here and there, hurdling fences, leaping over hedges and climbing trees as he helped hang Japanese lanterns. Side-by-side with the workmen, he was hammering, nailing, sawing until at last the enormous front lawn was changed into an open-air theater in the classic Greek tradition.

The formal lawn was about an acre in size, a smooth, green oval of grass surrounded by a wide, gravel drive. The house was on the other side of the drive, rising above the oval on a slightly raised mound like a jewel set in a ring. The lawn was bordered all around by trees, every other a white birch, and in front of the trees were gardens of peonies and roses.

On the night of the fete it was a beautiful sight, with the trees hung with fairy lights glowing in the darkness and the spotlights falling on the emerald carpet of grass. Here and there, flower beds were lighted, making bright splashes of color, and the driveway looked white as snow at night. The stage, erected on the lawn, was banked by huge, dark trees and green shrubbery, before which stood white marble Grecian statues brought from the house, and even the tall, cardboard Doric columns looked real. Over the stage, as if by design, a full moon rose like a great, polished opal, and magnolia blossoms shone pale and translucent in the half darkness.

When the dancers arrived and unpacked their costumes in the spare room, we discovered to our surprise that they were made of gray cheesecloth with frayed and ragged hems, but on the stage they appeared gossamer as they floated in the moonlight. The young girls of the chorus wore them short, just below the knees, with a cord crossed over their breasts and around their waists. As Greek music was never considered a great art, Uncle Demetrius dispensed with any attempt to emulate it, and had instead a small orchestra consisting of piano, violin and flute to which the girls danced as they held their arms over their heads or made graceful turns and dips and flying leaps across the stage.

The program consisted of several excerpts from the Greek tragedies of Euripides and Sophocles, after which a man got up and made quite a speech about the Armenians and their plight, and ended by quoting from their "Hymn To Liberty."

Mama sang, and a man sang, and someone played a piano solo and someone played the violin. I do not recall all the numbers on the program, but I do remember a man got up and paid a great tribute to Uncle Demetrius, listing all the honors he had received from the Greek government, and mentioning the fact that he had come to America a poor boy, yet only recently had sent money to his home town in Thessaley to have a huge clock built in the town square. He said this showed a noble and generous nature, and everyone should try to emulate this gracious spirit and Give Till It Hurt.

The fete was a great success, and when it was over Mama and Auntie said the receipts exceeded their fondest hopes and were so overjoyed that we were allowed to eat as much Neapolitan ice cream as we desired. We were almost as happy as Mama and Auntie, for we felt that now all the starving Armenians would have food and clothing, and the hollow-eyed children would grow fat and merry.

The next day we discovered that some of the dancers, in their hurry to leave, had forgotten their costumes. Artemis, Pericles and I immediately dressed

up in them and danced on the front lawn, imitating the same upheld arms, dips and flying leaps of the girls in the chorus the night before.

We must have made a pretty and appealing picture, for Auntie was having a visitor that day, an artist named Dawson-Dawson Watson (a name I found irresistible, even then), and as he sat talking with her on the porch, he found his paints and brushes and depicted a small, lovely scene of the three of us dancing in the sunlight.

We were enchanted with the picture, never having been painted in oils before, and often went to look at it as it hung on the wall in the parlor, amazed and awed that the graceful figures were really ourselves. Now, more than ever, we loved dressing up in the costumes, playing we were Greek dancers.

Then one day soon after the fete, Thea came upon us cavorting on the lawn and stood watching us in our frayed cheesecloth. She picked up the clothes we had carelessly thrown on the grass when we changed into the costumes, folded them neatly and laid them on a bench. Meanwhile she informed us it was just such thin rags as we were wearing that the starving Armenians wore in subzero weather. She said that the money from the fete was only a drop in the bucket compared to what they needed, and she suggested we think of them in their miserable garb, huddled together in the snow and sleet, every time we put on our warm, woolen, fur-trimmed winter coats and the long underwear we hated. "May you never have less," she said. Then, picking up a sock and shaking it free of grass, she announced sadly that the starving Armenians would give anything for a sock to cover their bones.

After that we put away the costumes, and even the picture by Dawson-Dawson Watson seemed rather dreary.

Ma-Ma

ON HOLIDAYS, such as Easter or Christmas, the family gathering at Parnassus expanded to include Papa's mother and father and his brothers, Epimandes and Miltiades, as well as his sister, Maritza. These, together with Papa and Mama, we three children, Uncle John and his American wife, Henrietta, Uncle Themistocles, Aunt Eurydice and her husband and two children, besides Auntie and Uncle Demetrius and their four children, Aphrodite, Achilles, Demosthenes and Aristotle, plus Thea and Grandfather, composed a formidable group.

Of all these relatives—even including Grandfather and Uncle Demetrius and making every allowance for the fact that there is safety in numbers—none could escape the impact of Papa's mother, my Grandmother

Pasmezoglu, who was no more than five feet tall. This imperious little woman was the epitome of willful temperament. She had been considered a great beauty in her day and had been noted for her beautiful hands with their almond-shaped nails, her lovely hazel eyes and her perfect profile. She had been, but was no more, a wealthy woman, and all of her life she had been used to having her own way through the power of money, the power of beauty and the power of her position in the family as Ma-Ma.

She had come to this country from Smyrna, in Turkey, where Papa's father had had a prosperous silk manufacturing business. Papa had gone to school at the American College in Athens, for the family was Greek though their home was in Turkey. Papa, being the eldest son, was given certain privileges not enjoyed by his younger brothers, who lacked this high station. At home he had his own suite of rooms, his own servant, his own horse and, in general, was treated as a kind of prince consort in the family. Grandmother was always fond of relating the fact that when he was born she threw gold coins to the peasants from her balcony.

At any rate, when Papa graduated from college, he made up his mind to come to America, where the Greek consul from St. Louis (Uncle Demetrius) promised to look out for him. He was thus given a job at the St. Louis World's Fair as head of the Olympic Games as a start in the right direction, and Uncle Demetrius took him under his wing as a great favor to Papa's anxious family. At Parnassus Papa met

Mama, fell madly in love with her and proposed. Grandfather approved and married them himself.

Soon after, in a skirmish with the Turks, during which their home as well as their factories were burned and the business ruined, the rest of the Pasme-zoglu family followed in Papa's footsteps and came to America.

Grandmother made this move with ice in her heart. To be banished to the wastelands of Siberia could not have been a more shattering blow. As a matter of fact, for Grandmother it might have been a little more desirable, for Siberia is connected with Europe, while, in her opinion, America was a faraway land, crude in its immaturity and peopled by brash foreigners who lacked the refinements of ancient civilizations.

Whatever Grandmother thought of the Americans, the Americans were happily spared from discovering, for she ensconced herself in St. Louis, there to remain aloof (so far as self-preservation would allow) from anything even remotely connected with the United States. In this way she was very much like Thea, whose attitude was one of extreme hostility to any-thing Hellenic.

I used to watch them eying each other across a room, these two women so antagonistic to each other, yet so alike in the measure of their intolerance—Thea, with her mail-slot mouth and turned-up nose, and Grandmother, the vestiges of her beauty still clinging in her finely drawn profile and her lovely hazel eyes beneath silvery hair, parted in the middle and worn in a knot low at the back of her neck. Fortunately they never spoke to each other, but simply gazed across the room in a kind of incurious contempt—one disdainfully observing the American in her midst, the other leveling her eyes on another foreigner in the house.

Grandmother was extremely vain, volatile and vastly spoiled. Thus, when balked in one of her aims, she would simply take to the floor, where she would lie down and scream. It was impossible to cope with her in any way other than to indulge her, for the rule about filial respect pertained whether the parent was right or wrong. She had been known, on many an occasion, to enter our house in St. Louis and fire all the servants in one sweeping gesture because she did not consider their work efficient. Mama, being practical as well as respectful, would hire them all back a few hours later, but while Grandmother was present, Grandmother was in command.

Her husband, Papa's father, was a quiet, gentle man who did not dare rebuke her and took refuge in silence and an early death. Her sons, Miltiades and Epimandes, were her slaves and her daughter, Maritza, her nursemaid, for Grandmother, among other things, was a hypochondriac, and one clutch at her breast would send Maritza scurrying to her side. Only Papa escaped, for he was married and did not live with her, but even so she would often descend upon his house, a tiny, handsome woman in black velvet and a chain of emeralds and like some terrible fairy queen issue edicts and commands. If it had not been for Papa's being her son, I think Mama would have come to terms with her, but as it was, she simply

accepted what she must have considered a most trying mother-in-law.

Whenever she saw us, she burst into tears, clutching us to her bosom and lamenting inconsolably that
we were cold and unaffectionate. For this she blamed
Mama, implying that she had turned us against her.
This was not true, for Mama did no such thing, herself belonging to the school that believed respect for
one's elders to be mandatory. We were simply scared
to death of Grandmother, both of her temper, which
was incomprehensible to us, and of her devotion, for
in the latter she would smother us with kisses, hold us
in an iron embrace and drown us in tears.

For myself, my reaction was simple. I hated her.
Mama said I *must* not, it was wrong and wicked—but
I did. Mama said she was very emotional and had
gone through an ordeal with the Turks, and I must try
to understand. But I did not understand. I thought
that all the Americans she hated were much, much
nicer than she was and that they were lucky not to
have her for a grandmother. I hated her wet kisses,
and when she hugged me I felt as if I were going down
in a sea of dough for she had ponderous soft
breasts and fleshy arms, though her hands dug into me
like iron claws. I just hated her with simple childlike
clarity of mind, and nothing Mama said could change
that. Yet for all I know, Artemis and Pericles felt no
such malevolence, only evincing at times a normal
terror.

Mama always said that Aunt Maritza was the most
beautiful young girl she had ever seen. Indeed, she

had a mass of jet-black hair, a flawless, ivory skin, eyes like brown velvet and her mother's perfect profile. She was docile and subservient, as might be expected, a shadowy figure in the background of her mother's dynamic personality. I suppose for this reason her beauty did not make an impression on us, although we loved her dearly, for she was always kind and gentle.

She was never without her mother. Ever present, quick to find her shawl, her medicine, the little pillow she carried wherever she went, alert to the tiniest flicker of pain, a look of discomfort, the sudden clutch of hand to heart, she would rush to her mother's side.

"Ah, Ma-Ma," she would whisper, kneeling by her side. "You are ill again." And she would chafe her wrists as tears brimmed in her soft, brown eyes.

At these times Mama and Auntie would look at each other wordlessly, but their silence bespoke a volume. I understood what they meant, for I had overheard enough to know they considered Maritza's only escape was to marry. Yet she had received several proposals from young men, all of whom Grandmother considered unworthy. After talking with them she soon discouraged the hopes as well as the desires of the young aspirants, and they went away to return no more. Grandmother was simply of the opinion that only royalty was good enough for her daughter, and that seemed to settle the matter. This situation continued until the day Grandmother died, whereupon, in an unprecedented burst of independence soon after, Aunt Maritza (already in her fifties) up and married a local tradesman without consulting anyone. Constrained to spend the rest of her life without the purple, she made a very nice thing of it, as far as I know.

Grandmother's temper fits always preceded her illnesses and were the result of a notion she had that her wishes were being ignored. She contained an enormous, portentous ego, which sustained itself in a simple, innocent question: "How can Ma-Ma be wrong?" How indeed? How can heaven be wrong? Can infinite wisdom be wrong? One does not argue with omnipotence. When her children had succeeded in calming her down, when the smelling salts had been applied, when Grandmother had gotten her way, she would find her breath and say serenely, "I am glad you have all come to your senses at last." And then, lifting her shoulders and spreading her hands wide, she would ask, "After all, how can Ma-Ma be wrong?"

If Aunt Maritza and my uncles Epimandes and Miltiades were her slaves, Papa was no less the victim of her tyranny whenever he was on hand. Weeping, wailing and wallowing in self-pity, she would clutch his hand while he soothed her with promises that her wishes would be complied with.

"There, there, Ma-Ma," he would say, chafing her wrists as she lay prone, "we will take care of it...." and Grandmother would slowly and reluctantly recover.

One day, however, she met her match—a man who took her terrible temper for exactly what it was, the outburst of a spoiled and selfish child, and treated it in a manner both simple and efficient.

It was a holiday at Parnassus, and Grandmother,

who was expected to spend the night, suddenly and ceremoniously announced her desire to be driven back to St. Louis. It was a stormy night, with ice and snow and a bitter wind that whipped across the countryside. Despite the inclement weather, Uncle Demetrius sent word to the stable to hitch the horses to the carriage and make ready to drive into town. A few minutes later there was a knock at the front door, and the driver stepped inside, a gale of wind blowing the door shut behind him.

He was a Swede, a man of few words and, hat in hand, he simply announced that it would be impossible to make the journey. Not only were the roads too icy but one of the horses was sick.

Grandmother did not understand English (refusing to learn was a self-devised banner she flew for her country) and was merely aware she was being balked. She flared up instantly and, in spite of a great deal of excited interpreting, her rage began to mount and she was soon stamping her foot and demanding obeisance.

The driver looked at her incredulously, naturally unable to understand such antics in the face of an unalterable fact. Finally, when she lay down on the floor and screamed, he simply looked around, saw a pitcher of water on a table near by and pitched its contents full upon Grandmother—assuming, I imagine, that he was acting heroically in a moment of crisis.

Dead silence fell upon the room. Grandmother's screaming stopped as suddenly as if a valve had been turned off. In the terrible hush, Auntie nudged the driver gently toward the door and out into the night.

Everyone was aghast and transfixed. Then, in the next moment, Maritza became electrified and rushed to her side with smelling salts. Miltiades and Epimandes fell to their knees beside her and rubbed her wrists and mopped her brow. Papa wrung his hands over her prostrate body in anguish. Still all was silence. Grandmother was, to all intents and purposes, in shock.

Nevertheless it was impossible to comply with her desires, and there was nothing to be gained by remaining on the floor. At length her eyelids flickered and, gasping for breath and clutching her heart, she allowed herself to be helped to a chair by her four devoted children. Then, sinking down into it and breathing heavily, she at last found her voice and what, I suppose, she considered a nominal victory.

"So *this*," she said, with a triumphant expression of vindication, "is the way men treat women in America."

It implied, of course, that in this country they went about unscathed after throwing cold water in women's faces, while in Greece she could have them beheaded for such barbarism.

The Jewel Box

ON THE second floor of the octagonal house a small foyer, which lead to one of the sleeping porches, was called the Medicine Room, for it contained a tall, golden-oak medicine chest as well as built-in cabinet for extra bedding, ice bags, heating pads and the like. The medicine chest contained many agents for curing sicknesses and ailments, but along with such standard properties as iodine, castor oil, rubbing alcohol and so forth, there was a special shelf for the medicines Mama always packed for us when we went away for the summer. This shelf was arrayed with many bottles and small boxes held dear to Mama's heart, and without which she would never have allowed us out of her sight.

There was Aristos Powder for Wounds, to be lavishly applied in the event of a scratch—something called, quite simply, Pink Pills for Pale People, which was very popular with Mama—a bottle of Dobel's Solution for sore throats—Alcock's Porous Plasters to be applied to the chest and back when suffering from bronchitis—Gleason's Oil ("Good for Man or Beast") always handy for cuts and burns—and a bottle of dark-brown liquid called Valentine's Meat Juice to give us strength. And, of course, there was such standard equipment as camomile tea, sulphur and molasses, Carter's Little Liver Pills, Castoria and Peptenzime.

Among all these things there was always a small, lavender box which contained sweetish, purple pills, which Mama occasionally told us to chew up and swallow. I hated these things, for they stuck in the teeth and had a sickeningly sweet perfume odor as well as a taste which I have ever since associated with the color lavender. We called them Persian Pills, but lately I have begun to think my dislike was well-founded, for research leads me to believe that Persian was merely a childish mispronunciation of the word purging.

We liked to play doctor and nurse in this small foyer, for we could use the sleeping porch as an infirmary, and no one ever seemed to mind if we soiled a few bath towels or pillow cases as we applied streaks of colored chalk to one another's arms and legs to simulate wounds.

Of all the rooms on the second floor, however, none could compare with my aunt and uncle's bedchamber. This room was extremely rich and elegant in feeling and contained a huge, brass, canopied bed hung with embroidered, blue satin. At the head of the bed, against the wall, was a tapestry of cherubs and flowers, and at the windows there were lace curtains under the same embroidered, blue satin draperies held back with brass tiebacks. There were carved chests with marble tops, and crystal and silver dresser sets and chairs covered in pink and blue silk. In one corner a votive light burned night and day before an icon, for my aunt and uncle were very religious, and this gave their room a rather hallowed quality in spite of its luxuriousness.

We might have felt no particular enthusiasm for this room, it being one of those places, like the parlor, where children were expected to maintain a kind of decorous conduct, except that it contained one thing which, for sheer dramatic effect, was unequaled in our young lives.

This was a most unique hiding place for Auntie's jewel box. She was afraid of thieves, but as she wore her jewels often, she did not want to make continuous visits to a safe-deposit box at the bank. Therefore she and Uncle Demetrius devised this rather astonishing scheme to conceal them.

By removing several bricks from the fireplace in their bedroom, they were able to make an opening in the chimney large enough to allow an iron box to pass through. This box, when suspended by a chain with one end anchored to a large hook inside the chimney, could then be let down the dark passage or pulled up at will. To disguise the hiding place, the bricks were merely replaced. Naturally, this gave the whole room an air of mystery and suspense, as we thought of the iron box dangling by its chain in the darkness of the chimney and of the horrifying disaster if it should fall.

After we were sworn to secrecy concerning the hiding place of the jewels, we were occasionally allowed to watch the operation in motion. Uncle Demetrius, knowing well the effect of this little drama upon us, would play it to the hilt.

Calling us into the room, he would then look about furtively, draw the curtains and lock the door. We would watch in awe and suspense as he knelt before the fireplace, still darting his eyes from side-to-side and occasionally jumping up to put his ear to the door. Auntie, impatient in her evening dress, would tap her foot as he played this game, but she too, understanding our fascination, never asked him to hurry. Now he would cautiously remove the bricks, one by one, asking over his shoulder if we thought the jewels would still be there, or if they had been stolen, or if, perchance, the box had fallen from its chain, only to be lost in the cavernous darkness beneath. Our eyes round, we would hold our breaths and inch nearer and nearer to look over his shoulder.

At last, the bricks removed, he would reach in and, hand over hand, as if the box were some pirates' treasure hove from the sea, pull it up to the light of day.

"Aha!" he would cry, unhooking it and placing it on a table to unlock, "now we shall see if any villains have been about!"

He would open the box with a flourish, and there, in the light from the brass chandelier that hung over the center table, the jewels would shimmer and glow in their iron box.

At this point Auntie would interfere in the drama of the moment by simply putting her hand in the box and, in a most unsuspenseful manner, selecting the rings or pins she wanted to wear.

She always looked very beautiful. Sometimes she wore a long, flowing, electric-blue velvet evening cape over a black net dress trimmed with jet. Then she would wear egrets in her hair or a tiara adorned with a small diamond crown. At other times she might have on a suit I loved. It was olive-green broadcloth, and with it she always wore a huge beaver hat trimmed with pink roses, and a beaver stole. Sometimes she wore a mink cape and plumes in her hat, but whatever it was, she looked beautiful.

This was only a fleeting thought with us, however, as we waited for her to close the box and for Uncle Demetrius to go on to the next act of this exciting drama.

With the same furtive alarm he would return the box to its hiding place. Down it would go, down, down to the lost and dark regions below, suspended by its iron chain, while we three crowded round, our heads craned on our little necks to see the last brick carefully replaced.

How imaginative and adorable this darling man could be! He had such feeling for the things that stir the minds of children and such heart for **the** things that bring them pleasure! I recall him all these years later with memories that cannot help but bring a smile, for there was whimsy in him, and this is a quality noticeably lacking in today's worrisome world.

Men Like Girls to be Pretty

ASIDE from Christmas day, there never was a time so festive at Parnassus as when a great party was held. At these times the reception hall was used for dancing, the Billiard Room, parlor and dining room were all opened and filled with elegantly dressed people and the entire house was a bower of flowers and potted palms. From the very cupola, the fabulous three-tiered chandelier burst into lighted globes and shimmering prisms, like an enormous gold and diamond pendant. All this brilliance, plus the laughter and music, seemed to fill the house with radiance and splendor, much as some women, bedecked in jewels, reflect a certain illumination from the gems they are wearing and become, for the time being, possessed of a gilded charm. Thus at these times Parnassus would

113

become an enchanted fairy castle touched with magic.

When Cousin Aphrodite would dress for one of these affairs, Artemis, Pericles and I would all gather in her room and sit on her bed to watch in profound admiration. She would come in from her bath wearing a camisole and embroidered petticoat over a corset, and everything was trimmed with lace and blue satin ribbons. Then she would begin with her nails. I seem to recall she used some sort of red salve around the cuticles to give them a deep look and a white paste behind the tips. After this she would buff and buff and buff, applying a sort of pink powder to the long, chamois-covered ivory buffer, which would succeed in making each nail glow like a pearl.

Her bureau was covered with ivory receptacles, one of which was a box with a hole in the top called a hair receiver. Another contained white talcum powder. She had a large ivory mirror, brush and comb as well as buttonhook, nail file and glove stretcher. There were also several crystal bottles, one of which contained lavender water, another glycerine and rose water for chapped hands.

After her nails she would do her face. This process, compared with today's standards, was rather unimaginative. She was just lucky enough to be born beautiful, for there was practically nothing at her disposal to enhance nature's gifts. She would pinch her cheeks to make them pink and bite her lips to make them red, after which she simply powdered her nose with a little talcum.

Arranging her hair came next, and consisted of

much brushing and combing and frizzing in order to form two puffs over each ear known, revoltingly, as cootie cages. Once these were in place, the rest of the hair was drawn back to a knot and decorated with combs or flowers. She had little tricks, such as coaxing a wisp of hair out here and there to make an innocent curl (known as a beau-catcher), or tucking a small piece of cotton soaked in cologne in the bodice of her camisole.

All of these things seemed to us not only glamorous and charming but rather wicked as well. Privately, we discussed whether or not she were a vamp, for when she dressed she seemed bemused and sometimes did not answer our questions, as if she were living in some private, secret dream of her own—which no doubt she was.

All of her dresses were beautiful to us, but one I remember in particular was made of pink silk with a high bodice and a pale-blue satin sash. It had an overskirt of tulle embroidered with little seed pearls and butterflies made of iridescent sequins and bugle beads. The whole thing fell gracefully to her ankles.

Whenever Cousin Aphrodite chose this dress, I was always happy, for with it she wore flesh-colored silk stockings and silver slippers with little Louis heels, which I considered utterly ravishing. Once when I looked downstairs through the banisters at the top of the steps and saw her sitting below in the reception hall with a young man, I noticed that she had crossed her knees so that the silver slipper swung prominently into view, and I thought this very clever of her. But most of all it established firmly in my mind, once and for all, that she was, indeed, a vamp.

Our position at the top of the steps was never questioned. Thea would always bring us ice cream and cake, and there we would sit among the potted palms, peering through the banisters at the dancing couples going round and round to a waltz or back and forth and sideways to a two-step. The man always let one hand rest lightly on his partner's waist while his left arm was stretched out straight and high and moved up and down in a pumping motion, as they moved over the floor to the tunes of "Dardanella," "Smiles," "K-K-K-Katie" or "Say It With Music."

Thea always sat in one corner of the reception hall in old-fashioned, black taffeta, looking on placidly but with a slight hint of suppressed disapproval on her lips. She considered modern youth headed for the dogs, and said so in no uncertain terms. When now and then a couple would wander out to the porch to sit on the swing, talking in the half-light, Thea would turn her head and look after them, her eyebrows lifted and her smile bitter. As she had had the misfortune to be taken in by the Dirty Yellow Dog, who had employed just such tricks of seduction in his courtship, it was her opinion that any man worth his salt would come to the point at once by making a businesslike offer of marriage. She did not go along with what she termed "a lot of fol-de-rol."

We could see and hear almost everything that went on from our vantage point in the upstairs hall, for the banisters went around the whole second floor, and we could move about so that all downstairs was like a stage with seats on every side. Music and laughter and bits of conversation floated up to us, and often we saw and heard things that other, less fortunate, spectators might miss.

If the party were given for Aphrodite, Auntie and Uncle Demetrius were always present as chaperones, sitting primly on chairs in the hall and keeping a sharp eye out to see that the young couples were comporting themselves in a seemly and moral manner. Auntie always insisted on spotting Aphrodite's parties with a young Greek here and there whom she thought would make a lovely husband for her daughter, and she often directed her attention to them, hoping they would think of her as a lovely mother-in-law. Thus, while she smiled pleasantly at everyone at the party, she smiled warmly at the Greeks, bending her head now and then in a gesture of special approval. Meanwhile, she and Uncle Demetrius were on guard to squash any sign of misdemeanor on the part of the not-so-reliable Americans.

I remember only one occasion when their presence did not serve wholly to mollify a tendency toward impropriety, and I was thrilled to be at my station at the top of the stairs to see and hear the whole thing.

One of the young men, it seems, had taken upon himself to have a few glasses of wine from one of the decanters on the sideboard in the dining room and, thus fortified, had attempted, in rather boisterous fashion, to kiss one of the girls on the dance floor. She giggled and squealed and then, catching my aunt and uncle's horrified expressions, ran from the dance floor and up the stairs, he hard on her heels. At the foot of the steps he stood calling noisily up to her.

Uncle Demetrius now rose to the occasion and, leaving Auntie frozen in her chair, stalked across the dance floor and took the young man by the arm.

"You will find your hat and coat," he said, "and leave these premises at once. We will see that your partner is driven home."

Abashed, the young man slunk away while we pushed our faces closer to the banister in order not to miss the rest. A few couples near by heard the admonishment and quavered, but in general the party went on gaily just as if lava were not erupting at its very core—for Uncle Demetrius was white with anger and his very beard shook.

Now Auntie, having gathered her strength, crooked a finger to Aphrodite as she danced by and whispered a few words which sent our cousin scurrying up the stairs, holding her skirts in her hands. We moved back into the recesses of the hall in order to hear without being seen.

The girl stood quavering beside a potted palm.

"Papa sent him home," Aphrodite whispered excitedly, "and Mama is having a conniption fit! What made him do it?"

The girl shook her head and said she didn't know.

"Mama said he drank some of Papa's wine! We'll have to drive you home."

The girl said she couldn't go downstairs, she was

much too embarrassed, and what would her mother say when she came home without her escort?

"Besides," she cried tragically, "I love him!"

Aphrodite thought this over and finally came to a conclusion.

"You go in my bedroom and go to bed," she said. "I'll say you have a headache, and you can stay overnight with me. I'll explain everything to Mama. After all, it's not *your* fault he was intoxicated."

"But he'll never take me out again!" wailed the girl, wringing her hands and weeping. "Your father humiliated him!" Then, angrily she added, "Honestly, Aphro, what difference did it make? We were only having a little fun. Your parents are sticks-in-the-mud! They sit and watch everything, and it's just an old-fashioned Greek idea, and I don't see how you can stand it."

How many times I had heard Aphrodite complain about this very thing, but suddenly she now took a loyal stand for her family.

"My mother and father are not sticks-in-the-mud," she said coldly. "And they're not old-fashioned, either. Maybe they do things different than we do, but you're a fool. That's no way to get a man—letting him maul you and giggling and acting as if you like it. If you want to get a man, you have to be cool. Maybe flirt a little, but you have to be cool. . . ."

The girl just looked at Aphrodite and blinked. She seemed to be considering a system, employed by an expert, which was entirely new to her.

"If you're not a *lady*," said our cousin grandly, "men won't respect you." She gave her friend a little smile and then added gently, "Now you just go to my room and go to sleep. I'll take care of everything." She started away and then thought of something else and added, over her shoulder, "If he doesn't like it, tell him to go to grass. There are lots of other pebbles on the beach!"

She swept down the stairs between the potted palms and went over and whispered to her mother. In a few minutes Auntie and Uncle Demetrius were smiling serenely again, and the party went on as the orchestra played.

We at the top of the steps were, of course, thrilled. And as we realized that nothing else could possibly occur that would compare with the scene we had just witnessed, we went to bed. There we whispered in the darkness and mulled over the close brush we had had with sin and the pearls of wisdom we had just heard on the subject of men.

Since our little brother, Pericles, was the only available male in our midst, Artemis and I asked his opinion on the subject. Whereupon he issued this sage advice: "Men want girls to be pretty and grow in gardens like flowers, and you don't walk all over them and mash them."

The Decision

A FREQUENT visitor at Parnassus was a friend of Aphrodite's named Florence Grant, a director of physical education at Washington University and older than my cousin. Auntie highly approved this friendship, for Florence was dignified, quiet, sweet and intelligent, with dark, wavy hair and what my aunt called a noble face. She seldom called any face except a Greek face noble, but in the case of Florence Grant she made this concession to American physiognomy.

However, there was always the disturbing fact that this young woman had been the instigator of Aphrodite's desire to become a doctor, and Auntie was adamant in her refusal. But it was becoming increasingly apparent that, except for Grandfather, Auntie was

121

losing her allies. Mama had gone all out in favor of Aphrodite, and Uncle Demetrius, motivated by his passion for education, had taken up the cudgel in his daughter's behalf. Now there was Florence Grant.

My Aunt Elene had some very positive notions. One was that Isadora Duncan stole her vase (she borrowed a hand-painted Grecian urn for a dance prop and never returned it), and another was that Aphrodite would be happiest married to a Greek. Studying medicine, besides being entirely too progressive for Auntie's tastes, also contained the threat of throwing Aphrodite headlong into a classroom made up entirely of American males, for at that time there were no women in the medical school in St. Louis. These were the basic reasons for Auntie's refusal to give her consent. It was true that Auntie was losing ground, but as long as she had the church (Grandfather) on her side, she would never lose her grip.

Sometimes I would hear Aphrodite talking to Florence Grant as they sat together on the porch.

"It's the one thing in all the world I want," she would say. "I can't be just a nobody, Florence. Mama thinks painting and singing and playing the piano are enough for a woman—I mean besides getting married to a Greek and having babies. But that's not enough for me. I know I'd be a *good* doctor!"

"I think so, too," Florence would say. "I've always thought so. I've watched you all the way through school, and you haven't an ordinary mind. My dear, you *must* try to overcome your mother's opposition."

Then Aphrodite would always add, "I can't. She's

got Grandfather on her side. Even Papa admits you can't go over the church."

I used to wish they would stop talking about it because it made me feel sorry for everyone. I loved my Auntie and I loved my cousin Aphrodite but there it was. I thought it was like a stone wall that you could not climb over or go through or get around, and the best thing to do would be to walk away. But my cousin would not walk away, and my heart ached for her.

Poor Aphrodite, going off to college in the morning, so beautiful in a blue twill dress with a hobble skirt, a blue hat ornamented with an owl and a long, gray wolf stole over her shoulders, wore a grim and unhappy expression in those days. Her brows were almost always drawn together, her pretty mouth tight and quivering, her lovely eyes either filled with tears or filled with resentment.

Poor Aphrodite, going off to the theater with a gentleman caller and two of her brothers, dressed to the nines in green taffeta with high button shoes and a green velvet hat decorated with a Spanish comb, was beautiful but sad. The single, long, black curl that hung from the back of her neck and fell over one shoulder was no more wistful than she.

Poor Aphrodite. All summer she made Battenberg lace and painted china cuff links with pretty flowers and dutifully played the piano and sang, but her heart was not in it, and almost always she would end by crying or running up the stairs.

Florence Grant soothed her, and Mama soothed

her, and Uncle Demetrius soothed her, but all admitted she was fighting a losing battle. Those were trying times indeed, and a terrible gloom fell over Parnassus.

Then one Sunday afternoon the Metropolitan of Greece came to call on Grandfather and brought with him the Archbishop and two professors of theology. Now in Mama's opinion, people fell into four categories. They were refined, common, or scum of the earth. Then there were a group of people who had advanced beyond refinement and had attained astral heights in their chosen field or profession. These people were high mucky-mucks.

The Metropolitan of Greece was a high mucky-muck, and we were all swooshed into the bathroom by Thea on the eventful day to be washed and scrubbed and brushed within an inch of our lives. Thea did not go along with what she termed dern nonsense as far as the Metropolitan was concerned. She was anti so many things that were Greek that it was not surprising that she was unimpressed by this great and holy man. Nevertheless, she believed in cleanliness, which seemed to have established itself as a virtue both in the South and other parts of the world, and she took this opportunity to shine us up as if we were a set of silverware.

When he arrived with his entourage, the Metropolitan was a glorious sight in Prince Albert and top hat complete with clerical collar. As we had been schooled to do, Artemis and I went forward and curtsied and kissed his hand, after which Pericles bowed with one arm held straight to his side, the other behind his back, then also kissed his hand. The Metropolitan clucked us under the chin, blessed us and remarked that we were lovely children, after which we went and sat primly on a bench under a tree, while the grownups gathered on the lawn in chairs to have coffee and talk.

It was a beautiful sight, and we were glad to be allowed to remain. Vast trays of bacclava, a rich, sweet pastry were served. There were bowls of grapes and peaches and pears picked fresh from the orchards, slabs of white goat cheese and the huge silver coffee service gleaming in the afternoon sun. Mama and Auntie, dressed in summer voiles, wore their real pearls and their church smiles, rather smug expressions of mingled pride and sanctity. Papa and Uncle Demetrius were resplendent in frock coats and striped trousers, and our four cousins were beautifully polite and self-effacing. Hercules, the Saint Bernard dog, lay panting on the grass, his tongue as pink as watermelon, and a butterfly, dancing through the air, lighted on his brown and white back. The pungent smell of coffee and cigar smoke filled the air, and shafts of sunlight slanted through the trees.

They talked of many things, for the Metropolitan and his entourage were intellectual as well as holy men. They discussed Grandfather's history of religions, politics, the church and even music and art.

Presently I perceived, from my seat under the tree, that Auntie was nudging the conversation around to the subject of science, with the idea of settling the controversy over Aphrodite's career once and for all. The Metropolitan's opinion was looked upon as gospel, and once he put his stamp of disapproval on the idea, it would be considered illogical, unsavory and possibly even slightly immoral to discuss it further. Aphrodite would be forced to recognize this.

The Metropolitan, unaware of the trap, spoke broadly on the subject of science in relation to religion. He and Grandfather agreed that, although science would continually move forward because the mind of man is both seeking and progressive, there is something in the universe which remains unaltered by knowledge and unaffected by science—something of eternal value which would persist though man went back to the Dark Ages. They cited mother love, the courage of the martyrs, conscience and prayer as examples. Science, they agreed, could never surpass these human, basic values.

Auntie nodded her head in agreement, while Aphrodite trembled with apprehension.

Then Auntie said, "My daughter wishes to take up the profession of medicine." At this point she looked over at Aphrodite and smiled sweetly and benignly. "And for some time I have been in doubt about allowing her to take such a step. Do you not agree, as my father does, that it would be inadvisable?" Her whole expression was affirmative and indicated that a man who recognized the superiority of God over science would recognize, also, Aphrodite's folly.

The Metropolitan considered this and, for a few moments, seemed to be collecting his thoughts to meet this unexpected crisis. Everyone waited patiently while Aphrodite looked doomed.

I looked at everyone's faces. Auntie looked sweetly victorious. Uncle Demetrius looked patiently re- signed. Grandfather looked inquiring. Mama looked annoyed, as if once again women's rights were about to be impinged. Papa looked aloof.

Then the Metropolitan spoke.

"*Au contraire,*" he said. "I consider your daughter's desire very laudable. We are entering an age when women, as well as men, must learn to be self-reliant. Moreover, to be of service to man does not go against God's teachings, rather it goes hand in hand with them. I consider it a credit to your daughter that she desires to take up this profession, and I say 'Bravo!' "

Dead silence fell upon the little group on the lawn, silence that was almost a thud. Auntie, whose face had come slowly apart with the Metropolitan's words, now made every effort to rearrange it in an expression of polite acquiescence. She blinked her eyes and smoothed an eyebrow with one finger and touched her pearls tentatively. Uncle Demetrius frowned with something simulating deep thought, which was meant to disguise his relief. Grandfather nodded. Mama winked openly at Aphrodite, and Papa continued to look aloof. Everyone else simply sat still in classical positions of decorum.

Then Auntie said, with as much graciousness as she could muster, "I bow to your reverent judgment."

Thus the issue was finally and irrevocably settled by the highest church of Greece.

Greek Easter

GRANDFATHER, acknowledging an authority on mores greater than his own, took the Metropolitan's decision of Aphrodite's career with equanimity and simple grace. He advised her to pray for God's help in meeting so great a responsibility, and thereafter the matter was dropped.

There were some things, however, in which he brooked no interference, and one was the deportment of his family during the four-day ritual involved in the Greek Easter services.

These began on Thursday, at which point all butter, milk, eggs and meat were eliminated from the menu as well as all fowl, fish (except shellfish) and vinegar. This meant starting off the day with a breakfast of bread and water and a little fruit, after which we went to church. No sudden childhood malaise was expected to interfere at this time, and Mama gritted her teeth against diphtheria and whooping cough (to which she now added another, more deadly fear— empty stomach) as we stood in the warm and over- crowded church.

The next day, Good Friday, food was still at a minimum, for this was a period of fasting. Moreover, the family spent the time between church services in modest and seemly practices, such as strolling in the garden or reading the Bible. Music, card games of any kind, even laughing were frowned on, for this was a day of quiet mourning, and Grandfather was on the lookout for anyone who violated the occasion. Once when Artemis and Pericles and I thoughtlessly began a game of jacks on the South Porch, he came upon us unexpectedly and thrust his cane out to upset the ball and little metal gadgets with which we were playing and uttered but one word, "*Stasoo!*" which means "Halt!" and went on his way.

All Friday morning Mama and Auntie picked bas- kets of flowers to take to church, and when we arrived there was a bier with a picture of Christ laid in it, which all the ladies decorated with flowers. This was meant to symbolize the sepulcher, and members of the congregation, coming forth with bouquets and crosses of lilies and white roses and carnations, kissed the painting of Christ and made the sign of the cross.

All through the afternoon and evening we stood through a long service, holding candles, until at last the bier was lifted and a long procession was begun through the streets with members of the choir hold-

ing the coffin and everyone chanting *"Kyrie eleison!"*
which means "Lord have mercy!" It was a moody,
mournful service, and the night air was filled with the
sound of lamenting.

On Saturday, the longest day of all, we went back
to church, still fasting, from eleven in the morning
until midnight. Mama always gave us Valentine's
Meat Juice, a tonic dear to her heart, to assure us
strength for the long hours ahead. And she had been
able to prevail upon Grandfather in one small matter.
This was that, when giving us communion on this day,
he would use a different spoon for the wine than that
which he used for the rest of the congregation. Mama
had been aided and abetted by Aphrodite in this
matter, both of them contending that the same spoon
in so many different mouths could cause nothing less
than pestilence. When it came time for communion,
therefore, Grandfather always took a small, gold demi-
tasse spoon from the sleeve of his robe for our turn,
and Mama was greatly relieved by this small concession. For his own part, Grandfather always looked
rather furtive and unholy at this point, and I think the
whole procedure went against his grain.

All day Saturday the church was in subdued light,
and we all held unlighted candles and repeated words
of prayer and supplication after Grandfather. Though
children were permitted to sit through most of the
evening service, the grownups maintained a constant
standing position except when they knelt in prayer.
After a time, Grandfather would disappear out of
sight, and Mama would whisper to us that we could

sleep. Drowsy and hungry, we would close our eyes and curl up against one another in the pew, only to be awakened sometime later by a gentle nudge from Mama.

Now the double doors to the inner altar opened, and Grandfather came out, magnificent in his golden robes, holding a lighted candle. It was exactly midnight.

"*Thefta lavete phoss!*" he would cry, which means, "Come ye and take light!"

One by one the members of the congregation would come forward to light their candles, until the whole church glowed and shone with tiny, flickering, golden flames. Then Grandfather, face illumined, voice tremulous with emotion, would announce, "*Kristos anesti!*" which means, "Christ is risen!" It was exactly midnight.

No matter how tired we had been, this beautiful sight, together with the shining light in Grandfather's face and the joy in his voice as he stood before us in his embroidered, silken robes, his jeweled cross taking light from the hundreds of flames which formed a kind of halo around him, filled me, as nothing else ever could, with the joy of Easter. Moreover, the hardship we had endured seemed somehow fitting in this moment of revelation.

Perhaps it was the fact that it was our grandfather, who seemed, in this small instant, to be the Lord God Himself as he stood before us, that filled me with such thrilling exaltation. Perhaps it was that, awakening from deep sleep, the sudden, flickering flames had a magical effect. Or it may only have been that I was in a weakened condition, much as the aesthetics are, after a long fast. I cannot say. I only know that through all the years, no other Easter service had just the same effect upon me of joy and oneness with God.

Afterward, back at Parnassus, a feast was laid out. Every Greek delicacy, as well as American ones, were put on the table. There would be a baked ham, big and fat and golden, scored and glazed with honey and pineapple on its top—a tureen of chicken broth (Mama always said we must have a hot cup of something light, first, so as not to shock our empty stomachs)— little, triangular envelopes of the flakiest piecrust filled with chopped spinach and onions—goat cheese, anchovies and silvery sardelles and wonderful wrinkled, black Greek olives, a little bitter and delicately flavored with oil and garlic—tiny meat balls swimming in a bowl of hot egg and lemon sauce and served with rice—bacclava, rich and sweet with figs and nuts, and crullers, called *xerotigana,* so thin and fine and sweet they curled and dripped honey as they were lifted to the mouth. And, of course, in the middle of the table and on the sideboard between decanters filled with wine, there were always silver bowls heaped with dark, blood-red Easter eggs, polished with olive oil until they gleamed like rubies.

Before sitting down to this repast, Grandfather would say grace, and everyone would take one of these red eggs and, holding it in his hand, click it against the egg held by the person sitting next to him, saying as he did so, *"Kristos anesti!"*

The next day, Sunday morning, the rest of the eggs would be hidden, and we would hunt in the gardens for them while Thea looked on with approval, satisfied that at last a touch of Americana had entered the picture. At three o'clock we would go to church for the final Easter service.

Oddly enough, when our American friends spoke of Easter and merely mentioned, fleetingly, that they had gone to church for a few hours on Sunday, I never felt that the comparison was in any way strange.

But there was one thing that did strike me as awfully peculiar, and to this day I cannot accustom myself to such an odd practice.

They had orchid Easter eggs! They even had pink and blue and green and yellow ones.

I considered this then, and still do, very farfetched and un-Easterish.

Sin Is Sin

ALTHOUGH Mama put much stress on physical health, she was not one to let the mind go undernourished, and she was equally staunch in her determination to improve the intellect. "I know enough to know that I know nothing," she often quoted Socrates as saying, thus pointing out that, in order to reach such abysmal depths of ignorance, one must be of a very superior intelligence. (It was not until I was much older that I realized this is true.) Mama quoted the Greeks on every occasion to prove a point, and once attributed the saying "Give me liberty or give me death!" to Socrates just before he swallowed the hemlock.

In any case, she was tireless in assisting us toward mental improvement, and these intellectual pursuits encompassed the fields of philosophy, history, music and the arts. They most certainly did not include a knowledge of conception and birth, which phenomenon was clearly described and illustrated in one of Cousin Aphrodite's medical books. Since the Metropolitan's momentous decision, Aphrodite's room had gradually changed. Besides the pretty clothes and the blue-ribboned letters and the diary marked PRIVATE, she now had a leg bone and a human skull tossed casually on a chair and charts of the human body tacked to the wall. These full-sized torsos were not only without their clothes, they were without their skin as well, and their lungs, livers and hearts were all exposed to full view and painted in the most garish shades of red, blue and mottled purple. She even had a cage of guinea pigs, which she later removed to the cellar, and stacks of medical books scattered over her desk. (One of the immortal moments of my life was when I pilfered one of these journals one rainy afternoon and, risking holocaust and condemnation, hid in a dark closet and perused it by candlelight.)

Mama was of the opinion that any knowledge of sex was best acquired in the marriage bed, and, until that fatal hour, it should be held in escrow, like a dowry. Meantime it was her intention to guard our virginity as if it were the Kohinoor diamond.

She read us stories from the great operas, showed us pictures of great paintings and eulogized the place that Greece had once held in world history, often emphasizing our enormous luck in having been born with such a heritage. Mama really managed to make us feel it was a pretty inferior type mentality that didn't recognize the significance of our Hellenic background. Along these lines, she once related to us an example of Greek superiority at its finest, and although, at the time, we were awed by the majesty of the moment, I recall it today with much humor.

For some reason, Ma-Ma had found it necessary to betake herself to market in St. Louis. Having determined not to learn English beyond a few meager words and phrases, she was having a hard go of it with her order, and the grocer had difficulty trying to decode her requests. Two high school boys near by watched this small tragicomedy for a time, listening to Grandmother struggling with the language while the grocer valiantly attempted to interpret her meaning. The boys snickered and elbowed each other, whispering that she could not speak English. Then all at once Ma-Ma turned upon them and imperiously and indignantly challenged them thus: "Spik me one word Grik! *One word!*"

Mama said the boys, abashed and humiliated, unable to speak one word of Greek, made a hasty departure, and I have no doubt they did. But I doubt, as Mama always added, that they felt a remorseful lack of intellectual ability and a terrible sense of loss because they had not grasped this beautiful and ancient language.

We knew the stories of Greek mythology as some children know Mother Goose. I do not know how Mama got around sex in these tales, which are so filled with the complex involvements of the love instinct in human nature. All I know is that we listened innocently as Mama unraveled them, and we certainly thought nothing of it when she related the tale of King Minos' wife, who was overcome with such passionate lust for a bull that Daedalus, that skillful artificer, disguised her as a cow so that she might satisfy her rather astonishing desires. Furthermore, this arrangement proved so satisfactory that in due time she bore the Minotaur, who was half bull, half man.

As for the story of Venus, whose promiscuity was nothing if not multitudinous, I do not recall in what careful language Mama clothed this tale. But we did learn that Venus and Ares, having been discovered as lovers by Hephaestus, Venus' husband, were imprisoned in a great, golden net, which was thrown over them as they made love on the side of a mountain. In this rather shocking *flagrante delicto,* the trapped lover and the faithless wife were the cynosure of all eyes. Apparently such a lesson in the consequences of impropriety did little to uplift the morals of Venus, for she continued her cavorting, having love affairs and illegitimate children with Adonis, Hermes and Anchises. For some odd reason incompatable with fact, Venus wore the Girdle of Virtue, and Mama always emphasized this, making everything on the up-and-up.

I suppose Mama felt, and I think she was right, that stories of Greek mythology had a greater educational value than stories of "Miss Muffet" or "Mary, Mary, Quite Contrary." And, indeed, we found Mother Goose rather dull fare after some of the escapades of the gods and goddesses.

Not content with nurturing the body and the mind,

Mama also nurtured the purification of the soul, and thus we were often coached in purity, modesty and truthfulness. She believed in the existence of sin and did not have any truck at all with -ids or -isms, which are sometimes today considered excuses for unlawful or immoral conduct. Sin was sin. It was a sin to lie, a sin to steal, a sin to kill, a sin to commit adultery, etc., etc., etc. If you sinned and failed to repent, you burned in hell, and that was the end of it. The only way to reimburse God for an infraction of His rules was to confess to Mama, and this we were called upon to do once a month.

The procedure took place thus: One at a time we would be called into the bedroom, and there Mama, managing to look benign and at the same time imperious, would fold her hands in her lap and turn upon us a patient and listening expression. We would then enumerate our sins: it was we who broke the pitch fork, we who took Aphrodite's doreen, we who ate the extra cupcakes. Mama would always look sad as such confessions of guilt fell upon her ears, but then, smiling and kissing us, she would announce that we were now absolved, and bid us go play while the next culprit made his entrance into the confessional.

I find no fault with this procedure today, for as long as its quality of formidableness lasted, we were less wont to err than we might otherwise have been, and certainly it watered down some of our more barbaric impulses. Of course, the day came, as all such days must, when we made our own private bargains with God and left Mama out in the cold—but in our young and formative years she was, perhaps, better able to guide us.

I remember the day it befell me to confess about Aphrodite's medical book. Mama was in a spot for once, because part of the ritual was that no punishment would be involved once the truth was out. The sole burden lay in admitting to sin and exposing ourselves to the sorrow in Mama's eyes. I left this most wretched transgression to the last, however, and then spilled it out in one sentence, all the words running together.

"Ireadinthemedicalbookhowbabiesareborn."

Mama could not contain her horror and merely gasped, "What!?"

"Ireadinthemedicalbookhowbabiesareborn."

Then Mama just looked at me helplessly, as if I had gone right out and played catch with the Kohinoor diamond, and said, *"Dendrepesse!"* which means "For shame!" in Greek.

Let the Prime Minister Wait

MY AUNT ELENE was so beautiful and, seemingly, so fragile and delicately made, and she had such an air of elegance, that it was hard to believe she was a dedicated chicken farmer at heart. Nevertheless, we often saw her walking past the long, low, story-and-a-half building which was the chicken house, clad in an old, dark shirt, men's shoes and a straw, farmer's hat, while in each hand she carried a bucket of mash.

Breeding chickens was her hobby, and she had inveigled Uncle Demetrius into letting her have her way in this strange passion, for indeed it was rather unusual in those days for a woman of my aunt's station to take so active a part in the care and feeding of poultry. Nevertheless, she got her way, although Uncle Demetrius always took a rather dim view of the whole thing.

I thought her hobby very odd because she was mostly interested in things that had a Greek flavor or influence, and she seemed altogether out of character in this role. I do not know enough about chickens, nor was I ever interested in all the machinations involved in raising them, but the picture of Auntie in her strange garb, feeding and handling these birds as carefully and reverently as if they were babies, has remained with me through all the years.

They used to flutter all about her feet and she called, "Here chick-chick-chick!" and flung handfuls of feed to them in the yard. And sometimes, inside the building, we would come upon her kneeling in the sawdust to see that the small baby chicks, no bigger than a handful of down, were safely huddled under a sort of large heating lamp that hung suspended over their separate enclosure. In another part of the building, hens in a loft would be sitting on their nests, and roosters, strutting about and flapping their wings, would make strange, egotistical sounds like proud fathers. Auntie always called the most ostentatious of these male birds Alectryon, for it was he who, according to Greek mythology, tattle-taled on Venus and Ares and caused them to be trapped on the mountainside in the midst of their love-making. For this sneaky deed, Ares had Alectryon turned into a rooster.

The whole place smelled of feed and sawdust, a dry, pungent odor that mingled with a feathery, chicken smell. It clung in the nostrils long after one left the enclosure, and, for myself, I found it disagreeable and unpleasant.

Not so Auntie. She was happy in the chicken house —happier, I believe, than she was in the parlor. For she was attempting to raise some sort of prize fowl which would compete with one being nursed along by a neighboring farmer, and toward this end she spent many happy hours of the day. Or, at least, as many as Uncle Demetrius would spare her.

I thought the chickens were ugly, with their scrawny necks and their tiny, heavy-lidded eyes and their sharp, pointed beaks. I hated their legs and feet, covered with wrinkled skin, and their frightened, nervous bodies. Only the baby chicks appealed to me with their soft, yellow down and their smallness, but even they had the same peaked faces as their elders, pinched and wise in spite of their babyhood.

Auntie also kept incubators in the basement, expensive contraptions warmed inside by electricity, to hatch the eggs. She spent many hours over these, turning the eggs gently and calling us down to see them when they hatched. I used to stare in dutiful silence at the cracked eggs from which extended wet, feathered heads on little, skinny necks and mouths opened wide in a bright-red, diamond shape as if they came into the world ready to eat.

It seemed to me that chickens ate all the time. When they were not being fed, they were constantly picking at the ground with their beaks. And if one came near them they scurried away, making shrewish, nervous sounds like old ladies interrupted in some meaningless task, their stockings falling and wrinkling around their legs as they fled—flat-footed, graceless and in an absurd terror.

Nevertheless, and despite my antipathy for chickens, Auntie loved them, and it was difficult to tear her away from her hobby.

Thus one day Uncle Demetrius, after sending word down to the chicken house three different times, came himself to fetch her. He was dressed to the hilt, complete in top hat, Prince Albert and cane, and he was very much annoyed, his pointed beard and his waxed mustaches seeming to whisk about as he reprimanded her. For it seems they had an appointment to call on Eleutherios Venizelos, the Prime Minister of Greece, who was stopping in St. Louis on a grand tour across the United States.

Auntie, in her old farm clothes, soiled and grimy and divinely happy, did not look as if she could ever make herself presentable enough to call on such a dignified notable as this Greek statesman, and Uncle Demetrius was beside himself.

Auntie placated him and put down the bucket of mash she was carrying. Artemis, Pericles and I, who had been playing near by and overheard the conversation, now hurried after them into the house, hoping that since Auntie was going out we would have an opportunity to play the game about the jewel box.

Uncle Demetrius was much too upset to play games, however, and, despite the cool autumn afternoon, his face grew hot and flushed as he sat himself down in the reception hall to wait. He kept looking at his watch and then at the stairs as he tapped one spatted foot on the floor, and from time to time he would get up and pace back and forth, making little clucking sounds with his tongue.

"My wife," he said to us, having no one else on whom to vent his impatience, "has an obsession for these blasted chickens. Now how does she expect me to endure it? It's bad enough to wait until some ridiculous chicken has had her attention first. But at a time like this! Just imagine! The Prime Minister of Greece must also bide his time for a hen!"

He went on pacing back and forth, pointing his cane as if it were a baton.

"I've put up with this long enough! Do you realize that these chickens are beginning to take precedence over her own husband? And what's to become of her looks? Out in the hot sun all day! She's ruining herself!" He turned and looked at us threateningly, as if we were somehow in league with her.

"Now just you wait until she comes downstairs! I'll have a few things to say about this! She thinks she can hoodwink me with her airs and graces and have her own way about these infernal chickens, but I'll put a stop to it this time, you wait and see!"

Just at this moment, down the steps came Aunt Elene, looking as if she had never in her life lifted a finger for anything more strenuous than to slip on a ring. Only a half-hour ago she had been dressed like a farmer's wife, and now she looked like a queen. She wore a navy-blue tricolet dress and her short chinchilla cape and muff. Her hat was bright blue, adorned

with bird-of-paradise feathers, and she carried a blue and silver beaded bag. On her feet were black satin pumps with cut steel buckles.

I can see her as plainly today as I saw her then, for she was beautiful and she glittered, both with her diamonds and with her smile, which was as warm and bright as the autumn sunlight. Her cheeks were pink from the sun, and her hair curled bewitchingly around the blue hat, while her lovely, amber eyes twinkled softly at her husband.

When Uncle Demetrius saw her, he stopped pacing, and, although in his anxiety he had forgotten to take off his hat before, he took it off now as he watched her come down the steps. Then he offered her his arm and smiled adoringly at her as they went out of the house together and got into the waiting carriage and, leaving the chickens far behind, drove off to see His Excellency, the Prime Minister of Greece.

What Eleutherios Venizelos thought of my Aunt Elene I do not know. But of one thing I am sure. Unless she told him so, he never dreamed that she knew a Silver-Laced Wyandotte from a Black Minorca.

The Fortune

MAMA and Auntie were drinking Turkish coffee and eating grapes out in the hammocks under the chestnut trees. Lounging back in their white chitons against colored cushions, they held their arms curved upward in the air, dangling clusters of the purple fruit in their hands. They looked like illustrations in a book. Mama was very dark and European with her lush figure and her heavy-lidded eyes so deeply shadowed they seemed to be painted with kohl. Her hair, held high in a Psyche knot, gleamed blue-black against the silken ribbon wound three times around her head, and her skin seemed the color of ivory.

In the hammock near by Auntie reclined with a mandolin in her lap. She was taller and thinner than Mama, and her eyes and hair were a lighter shade.

147

She was a pure Grecian type, while Mama might easily have been French or Italian. She, too, wore her hair in the Psyche style, and the folds of her white garment fell over the side of the hammock almost to the ground.

In the background two enormous urns held aloft by iron griffins were filled with pink geraniums and petunias, and the branches overhead were clustered with golden, cone-shaped blossoms. Across the lawn, Hercules lumbered after a rabbit. Auntie plucked on her mandolin, touching her sandaled foot to the ground occasionally to keep the hammock in motion, and Mama sang a little Greek song in her beautiful voice. Two brilliant blue-green peacocks sauntered by, dragging their magnificent tails.

Somewhere near by, I sat under a tree, making a clover chain. My lap was filled with the tiny white flowers whose long green stems I methodically plaited together to form a necklace with which I intended to bedeck Mama when it was finished. I looked over and thought how pretty she was, lying there in the gently moving hammock.

It was late afternoon, coffee time, and two little cups rested upside down on a table near by. I knew what this meant, for scarcely an afternoon went by that Mama did not tell Auntie's fortune, and I loved to listen, for it was almost like hearing a story. I waited patiently, plaiting the green stems and occasionally holding up the chain to admire it.

Presently Auntie yawned and put the mandolin aside.

"Aren't you going to tell my fortune, sweetheart?" she asked.

"In a minute," said Mama. "The cups aren't dry."

Mama had learned to tell fortunes, from her grandmother, by peering into the round, concave depth of a cup from which Turkish coffee had been drunk. The thick brew left a dark-brown, lacy pattern on the inside, and Mama saw the future in this.

Nothing thrilled my Auntie so much as having her fortune told. She believed everything Mama predicted and waited patiently for each event to transpire. Mama always began by laughing and saying it was all nonsense, then grew more serious as she looked closely, pursing her lips and making little clucking sounds as she turned the cup.

Now Auntie could hardly wait for the cup to dry, but she tried to be patient. She knew that everything depended on the pattern being set, for should the cup be turned while the dregs were wet, the whole future might be thrown out of focus. There was nothing to do but wait.

She picked up her mandolin again and strummed idly, looking up through the branches at the blue sky.

"Whenever I see the sky so blue," she said, "it reminds me of Athens. There was never a sky so blue as the skies of Greece," she told Mama, who had been born in Rumania and had come to America when she was eight years old. It always seemed to Auntie that Mama had been cheated by fate because grandfather was officiating at a church in Bucharest at the time of

Mama's birth. She closed her eyes and began to quote from Byron:

> The isles of Greece! the isles of Greece!
> Where burning Sappho loved and sung,
>
> . . . .
> Where Delos rose, and Phoebus sprung!
> Eternal summer gilds them yet,
> But all, except their sun, is set . . .

"That's beautiful, darling," said Mama. "How Byron loved Greece!"

"Yes," said Auntie. "And he had a beautiful face, like a Greek god." She added, "I think it was criminal of the English to take his body back to that cold, foggy island after he died. The Greeks wanted him buried in the temple of Theseus in Athens, and I'm sure he would have preferred it."

"Oh I don't know," said Mama. "After all, he *was* an Englishman."

"Not in his heart," said Auntie. "He loved Greece."

It now occurred to her that the coffee cup must be dry, and she again urged Mama to tell her fortune. Mama reached over and picked up the little cup and gazed inside, turning it this way and that.

"What do you see?" asked Auntie, growing more animated as Mama grew more serious. "A trip?" For to my Aunt Elene, a trip was a joy unsurpassed.

"Oh, it's all nonsense," said Mama, looking up and smiling.

"Never mind," said Auntie. "Tell me what you see."

"Well, my dear," said Mama, thoughtfully, peering into the cup from which my aunt had drunk her coffee, "as a matter of fact I do see a trip. You and Demetrius are going out west, for I see hills and mountains and desert before you. . . . Yes. . . . Oh, my! Who is this handsome man in a tall silk hat? He is being very attentive to you. . . ."

They giggled like schoolgirls over the prospect of the handsome stranger, and then Mama went on, "Yes, I see a trip to the west and—" turning the cup slowly, the better to see the pattern—"here is a woman. She is very dark and has her arm around you. She has a pointed face and a thin mouth. You mustn't trust her."

"That must be Fortuna," said Auntie, gasping. "You've described her to a T."

"Now, I don't like this," Mama went on, still peering into the cup and frowning. "Someone is sick. I see a doctor. . . ." She considered for a while and then smiled. "However, it is nothing serious," she decided. "The doctor is laughing and chatting with you, which is a good sign." Then she shook her head in amazement. "Oh, and my dear, such a lot of money! It is everywhere around you!"

She went on and on, exhausting all the possibilities of the cup until Auntie had to be satisfied there was no more to tell.

The nicest thing about Mama's fortunes was that they almost always came true. Auntie did go out west as Mama predicted and came home to confide that the Greek consul in San Francisco had been both handsome and charming. Fortuna had, indeed, proved a false friend, and Uncle Demetrius had taken a cold. As for the money, there always seemed to be plenty of that.

But there was one fortune I heard Mama tell that Auntie didn't like.

"I see a young man," she said one afternoon after her customary prologue of insisting it was all nonsense, "who is being very attentive to Aphrodite."

"Is he a Greek?" asked Auntie at once. Now that she had lost the battle about Aphrodite's medical career, she staked all her chips on the fact that her daughter would marry a Greek.

"I don't think so," said Mama. "But, oh, my! He is *very* handsome!"

"Well, many of these American men are attentive to Aphrodite," suggested Auntie. "What is he up to?"

Mama peered closer into the cup and made a clucking sound.

"My goodness, he is *more* than attentive," she said, laughing lightly. "In fact, he is putting a ring on her finger. Aphrodite has on a wedding veil, what's more."

Auntie blanched.

"How do you know he is not a Greek?"

Mama frowned and shook her head slowly, still looking in the cup.

"Because he doesn't look like a Greek. Not at all, though as I say, he is very handsome. He appears to be of German descent."

This was too much for my Auntie.

"Impossible," she said. "I would never stand for it. Perhaps the cup is wet and you have got the future out of focus."

"The cup is not wet," said Mama, with such assurance that I wondered if she had not met Aphrodite's young man and was thus forearmed with fact.

"Then you are seeing the cup wrong," said Auntie.

"I certainly am not, Helen," said Mama. She never called Elene by her American name unless she was annoyed, and now, it seems, her ability was being questioned.

"I am not seeing the cup wrong," she said, miffed. She put it down and gazed off into space, looking dark and mysterious. "What's in the cup is in the cup." Then she turned back to her sister and shook her head. "Why does it matter so much to you if Aphrodite marries an American? Suppose she met a wonderful young man, a doctor like herself, who loved her very dearly . . ."

"Aphrodite is Greek," said my aunt flatly. "She should marry a Greek. It is the only way she will ever know true happiness. I think you saw the cup wrong."

"Very well," said Mama. "If you think so, I shall not go on."

My auntie was visibly disturbed. I knew she was thinking of all the fortunes which had come true: all the trips Mama said she would take—the weddings, the funerals, the christenings . . . the letters . . . the dark women and the light women in her life . . . the babies who were born and the unexpected messages she had received. Mama had predicted all these things and

all had come true. True, so far she had not gone back
to Greece . . . and there was the redheaded man with
glad tidings yet to come. . . . But on the whole . . . I
could see Auntie toying with the pros and cons of fortune and knew she would not be able to resist hearing
the rest of this one.

"Please go on, Penelope," she said at last.

"Very well," said Mama, mollified. She picked up
the cup again and looked inside.

"There are a great many people at the wedding,"
she began. "Many people and many flowers . . . I see
Demetrius and the boys . . . and a man with a beard.
I believe it is father. . . . And here you are!"

"Well?" asked Auntie.

"Why, you look beautiful," said Mama. "I have
never seen you look so beautiful and radiant. You are
very pleased. Extremely pleased."

"How do you know the man isn't Greek?" asked
Auntie feebly.

"Because I know it," said Mama. "The cup tells me
so. And it doesn't matter to you one bit. You are very
happy about this wedding."

Then Auntie, who was Mama's greatest fan and
had never in her life before suggested that a single
one of the forecasts might possibly fail to come true,
just made her mouth small and prim and said, "*En
theaffair an aleethis,*" which means, "Interesting if
true."

The Visitor

THERE was an island quality to our summers at Parnassus, a strange, idle, autonomous tendency to live with and within the property itself. Isolated as it was, bordered by trees and shrubs from other homes and families, it contained, within its own boundaries, a world of its own. As children we were, in a way, wholly removed from outside influence during the summertime.

Artemis, Pericles and I played together, unaware of the absence of other children, seemingly without need of any companionship beyond that which we had to give each other. We made our own laws, our own rules, our own regulations, and any quarrels which could not be settled amicably between ourselves were simply taken before Cousin Aristotle, much as some islanders take theirs before a medicine man.

156

We played games which required three, and we had
secret hiding places, secret treasures and special, secret words we used. A certain resinous substance
which exuded from the trunks of cherry trees and
formed itself in a fixed, shiny bulge was called the
Horse's Eye, for indeed it looked much like a horse's
eye, being brown in color, round and glistening. Mama
said this was a disease and forbade us to touch it, but
we liked to go and look at it, fascinated by its solemn,
watchful stare.

Contrary to her aversion to the Horse's Eye, Mama
believed that tar was good for the teeth and had no
objection when we wrapped this gummy substance
around a stick as it oozed up, hot and pungent in the
summer sun, between the flagstones outside the laundry house. When we had a fair-sized wad on the end
of a stick, we would chew it, and I can recall the taste
today—an acrid, tinny flavor, somewhat akin to the
smell of coal dust.

The summers were long and never lonely. We went
for hay rides, lying on our backs in the wagon, looking
up at the blue sky, breathing in the sweet, new-mown
smell. Sometimes the world was nothing but hay and
moving sky and the sound of horses' hoofs as we
jogged along, and I felt very small and isolated and
pretended I was an ant in the fields.

Sometimes we climbed into a cherry tree and, sitting high in the dark-green and red leafy branches, we
ate our way out. We took long walks with Demosthenes and gathered violets by the brook, and sometimes we went down to the pond to paddle in our bare

feet and listen to the reeds whisper, "King Midas has ass's ears," for Mama had told us that Midas had tried to conceal this disfigurement under a cap, but his barber, whom he had sworn to secrecy, had discovered it. The barber, bursting with a desire to tell the secret, could contain himself no longer and dug a hole in the ground into which he whispered the news. Reeds sprang up on the spot, and when the wind blew through them they whispered softly, "King Midas has ass's ears."

We loved to play in the arbor, where a trapeze hung from the centermost pinnacle, and in the barn and the laundry and the stable. All these outbuildings were built in the shape of a Greek cross, and all had small cupolas like the main house. There was a playhouse, which my cousins had used when they were small children, each owning a separate wing of the cross for his toys. This was now used as a sort of tool shed, but a huge swing remained in the center area, which was a replica of the octagonal hall, and here we would fly through the air with the greatest of ease.

We did everything together and accepted, without question, our interdependency and our own remote seclusion.

It was therefore an event of no little moment when one morning Pericles awakened me by tugging at my arm and, putting his finger to his lips, led me to the screen on the sleeping porch and pointed below, his heavy-lidded eyes following my gaze.

Standing there under a tree, doing nothing at all,

was a child. A girl. She had straight, nearly white hair cut in a Dutch bob, she wore a blue and white checked gingham dress, poorly made and of cheap fabric, and she was barefoot.

We stared at her for a long time as if, from the sea around us, some strange creature had been washed up on our island shore. At length we wakened Artemis and she, too, came and stared. Then in a frenzy we all three dressed and ran downstairs to make friends with the visitor.

We found her still standing under the magnolia tree doing nothing at all. All three of us came slowly upon her, then stopped and stared. She stared back. Finally, in the *entente cordiale* common to all children, Artemis broke the ice by asking, "What's your name?"

She did not answer, but looked at us meditatively and somewhat incuriously.

"Do you want to play?" asked Pericles.

No answer.

I decided to try my hand at sociability.

"Would you like to see my cousin's dead guinea pig?" I asked.

She now put her fist in her mouth, and her pale eyes sought the ground, the toes of one foot curling over the instep of the other.

"Don't you want to play?" asked Pericles.

The child took her fist away and said, quite simply and gravely, without lifting her eyes, "I dassn't."

"Dassn't?" exclaimed Artemis. "What's that mean?"

"Ma says I dassn't play with you."

We were so intrigued with this new word that we went into a whispered consultation.

"I think it means she *can't*," explained Artemis. "She dassn't play with us means she can't play with us. *Why* can't you?" she asked the child.

Now the girl raised her eyes defiantly.

"I told youse oncet. I ain't allowed."

We were charmed—not only with the child herself, at once so mysterious and so unprecedented (like Venus, springing from the head of Zeus, she had arrived unheralded, unsung and *in toto*), but with her strange, new vocabulary.

"Oh, come on," said Pericles. "If you don't want to see the dead guinea pig, I'll show you where we're digging to China." He reached out a hand to touch her, and in the same instant she was gone, darting away among the trees, a sprite with white hair and skinny legs around which flapped the blue and white gingham of her skirt.

We made a beeline for the house to clear up the mystery, and were told that she was the daughter of the new laundress. Auntie disclaimed any knowledge of why her mother wouldn't let her play with us, but told us her name was Flo and that people with hair that color were called albinos.

Flo herself explained the situation to us later, for as the days went by we pursued her so relentlessly and with such determination that she was at last able to overrule her mother.

"Ma says," Flo explained, as we generously divulged

all our secrets, our codes and our treasures, "Ma says youse is rich. She says it ain't fair to me."

We gravely accepted this explanation, having not the faintest notion of its meaning, merely delighted that the matter had been settled and our lives were allowed to profit by the windfall of her appearance.

Never had we had such a friend! In later years, when we were a little older, we were allowed to bring some of our friends from the city out for a week end, but on these occasions we always found that they were intrigued by the house and our relatives and our way of life. They found it unusual and sometimes even amazing. They asked questions constantly and responded in various ways: with awe, with incredulity, with ridicule, with curiosity, but never with anything less than a positive reaction.

With Flo *we* were the audience. We marveled at the world she lived in and besieged her with questions. She taught us many things that summer and told us strange tales, the like of which we had never heard before.

"I had a brother oncet. He went to war and the Huns shot him in the belly. All his guts came out. Ma says she ain't gonna rest until she gets aholt of a Hun and boils him alive. The reason she works is to get aholt of enough money to go to Germany and get aholt of a Hun. . . ."

When we showed her how the orange soda came out of a tap in the icebox, so that we could have as much as we desired by merely pressing a lever (a device Cousin Demosthenes had rigged up), she said,

"That reminds me of a saloon my Pa took me to, where they had one of them things, only beer came out. Ma said I dassn't go, but Pa picked me up right out of bed and took me with him. When Ma yelled, he bashed her one."

She told us about her sister, Marj, and her brother, Delmar.

They fought all the time. One morning Marj was filling out an application for a job and Delmar was looking over her shoulder. When she came to the space marked SEX, Delmar grabbed the pen and wrote *Seldom, but have been.*

"Marj gave him a belt in the face with her pocket-book and blood ran down. But all Del did was laugh."

Although we did not understand why Marj gave Delmar a belt in the face, we were enchanted. Our summer was sheer delight, for Flo had the magic quality of transporting us from our everyday world to a world peopled by strange creatures who spoke a new and fascinating language, and whose lives were filled with calamity and catastrophe. They performed deeds of wondrous prowess, and the feats of the gods on Olympus paled by comparison with the time Flo's Uncle Louie "took aholt of the doctor when Aunt Mable's baby was born blue and knocked him clean down the stairs."

Then one day she was gone. As unexpectedly as she had arrived, just as suddenly was she gone. All of Parnassus was stilled by the enormity of our loss, empty and silent without our friend. We were inconsolable and ran to Auntie weeping. Mama, who had been away on a trip to New York and had returned only a day or two before, came into the room and found us in despair.

She and Auntie looked at each other and shook their heads sadly and wisely, as if they had been in secret consultation and were not surprised.

"I ain't going to play outside no more!" wailed Artemis.

"You dassn't make us stay here without Flo!" I cried.

"I'll go find her and get aholt of her and I won't never leave her loose!" threatened Pericles.

Then Mama looked at Auntie, imperceptibly raising her eyebrows as she smiled faintly, and said, "*Xefortethichame en kero,*" which, translated literally, means, "We unloaded her in the nick of time!"

The Tenth Commandment

UNCLE Demetrius had certain Rules of Conduct by which he lived and by which he expected others to live. At one time he wrote them all down, very plainly in black crayon on a piece of cardboard, which he hung in the upstairs hall—a constant reminder to the wayward. They went like this:

NEVER SMOKE
NEVER GAMBLE
NEVER SWEAR
NEVER BE ENVIOUS
NEVER BE REVENGEFUL
NEVER ENTER A SALOON OR POOL PARLOR
NEVER NEGLECT THE CHURCH
NEVER NEGLECT YOUR MOTHER
NEVER BE EXTRAVAGANT

These oddly assorted nine commandments were put into effect at Parnassus, and Uncle Demetrius brooked no laxity with them. Because he felt that saloons and pool parlors were the habitats of scalawags and rowdies, he installed a billiard table in his library and kept wine on the sideboard for the free use of all. I know that he considered smoking bad for the health and often cited his own vigorous physical endurance as an example of abstinence from this vice. All of his Rules of Conduct were based on physical and spiritual growth, for there was nothing Uncle Demetrius hated so much as signs of weakness.

A particular sign of weakness, in his opinion, was extravagance, and he often lectured on the subject of waste. While he was a wealthy man and provided his family with every comfort and many luxuries, he was nevertheless moved, from time to time, to establish in their minds the value of thrift. Thus, while with one hand he spent freely, with the other he shook a finger at munificence. He was never content with anything less than the best, yet he felt there was a definite line to be drawn between excellence and extravagance.

Therefore, when he decided to take his family on a trip across the country to the west, the entire entourage to travel in the height of luxury, he went into a long exposition on costs and earnings and the necessity for each of his four children to help defray expenses. In other words, he informed them they would have to add to the kitty.

All that summer Aphrodite, Achilles, Demosthenes

and Aristotle set about earning money for the trek to California. Aphrodite grew mushrooms in the cellar and served them at every meal and sold them to her friends. They were as big as saucers and very succulent and brought a fine price. She also painted china cuff links and buttons which she sold, helped in the kitchen and made her own clothes. The boys worked in the orchards picking cherries and peaches and packing them in baskets which were taken to market and sold. They also collected eggs for the same purpose and helped milk the cows and worked in the fields. All summer long my cousins were very busy and industrious, and it never occurred to any of them to complain or to find anything absurd in the procedure.

Presuming they were growing spiritually, they were also growing physically in beauty and health. The boys were tanned and hard from climbing trees and working in the sun. Aphrodite wore the expression of a woman doing her bit—serene and dedicated. Every time she put a few dollars in the iron bank Uncle Demetrius kept for this purpose, she looked either like a pixy or a nun, depending on whether she had been selling painted buttons (which she loved) or washing dishes (which she hated).

As for Uncle Demetrius, he went about whisking his beard, his ruddy face aglow with delight as he observed his brood developing traits of industry, thrift and character.

Artemis, Pericles and I soon caught the bug and wished to be part of this program of fund raising. It seemed rather unfair that we should be left to idle our time in play while everyone else was so joyously slaving. We therefore went en masse to Uncle Demetrius one day, suggesting he take us along to California if we earned the money.

This, he explained, taking us all on his knees and kissing our necks, would be impossible. But if we would like to add something to the iron bank, he would bring us each a beautiful present when he came home.

Joy of joys! We now had reason to stop playing and work all summer, letting the pennies we earned clatter into the iron box. Auntie allowed us to make the beds, to pull dandelions out of the lawn, to help weed the strawberry patch, to count the silver when it was put away. We could also help churn butter, carry milk pails from the barn to the kitchen and feed the chickens. Anyone seeing us must have thought it odd that three small children, laboring so hard through one whole summer, were moved to sing as they slaved.

But we did. Uncle Demetrius, in his wonderful way, had given meaning and purpose to our days. It was an exciting new game, earning money, and filled us with a kind of proud importance. Sometimes we sang American songs as we marched along with our pails of warm, foamy milk from the barn. "Onward, Christian Soldiers!" we would warble in trio, our socks hanging down around our sandals, our hands grubby from the strawberry patch, our faces turned to the sky.

At other times, our backs aching as we filled basket

after basket with dandelions, we would burst into Greek songs—the "National Anthem" or *"Ageeaws Vassilius,"* a tune normally reserved for Greek New Year's morning. (Our American friends were always awed and a little mystified when we told them that on our first day of the year, January seven, we would jump out of bed and, still in our night clothes, go stand outside our parents' bedroom door, vocalizing this song at the tops of our voices. Finally Papa would come out in his nightshirt and give us each a gold piece. They learned the words and tried it on their families, but nothing ever came of it until one little girl thought up the idea of singing her father's college song, "Amherst, Dear Amherst," for which he gave her a dollar.)

In the beginning all went well. We would take our fistfuls of pennies to Uncle Demetrius, who would drop them one by one into the bank, crying, *"Fassuli fassuli ye meesi taw sacculi!"* which means "Bean by bean we fill the bag!"

At first there was always the dream of our reward, but as time went on the pennies themselves became more precious than the dream. We soon made up our minds that at the end of summer we would prefer to have our money rather than the surprise. And at length we began to quarrel among ourselves—who had worked the hardest, who had earned the most, who deserved the credit. We raced to do the job first, to get paid soonest, and we even asked for a raise and began to keep books. As time went on, everything we did or thought was in terms of money, and at night I would lie on the sleeping porch and dream of golden coins reaching the sky.

One of Uncle Demetrius' Rules of Conduct, NEVER NEGLECT THE CHURCH, necessitated a day of rest on Sunday and required that we put down our tools of labor. We resented this bitterly, for it put a temporary halt to our earning power, and when Mama and Papa came out on week ends, we stood around watching them play croquet or lawn tennis, and longed to get back to our moneygrubbing.

Mama and Auntie and Cousin Aphrodite and sometimes Aunt Eurydice would float over the grass in their sport dresses, always something with a nautical influence, like a sailor collar, and rather rakish hats to protect them from the sun. Playing croquet with the men, they would bend a little to give their mallets a mighty swing and send the wooden balls through the wickets. They would laugh a good deal and call out "Good shot!" to one another, just as they did at pocket billiards, and sip lemonade under the trees.

Sometimes Cousin Aphrodite and some of her friends would play tennis with Achilles, Demosthenes, Aristotle and Uncle Themistocles. At other times the whole family would group on the lawn, eating watermelon and making a pretty summer picture under the trees. Thea would put on her old-fashioned, white dress and bring her tatting, her shuttle working endlessly as she rocked and hummed. In the shade would lie Hercules, his mournful, red-rimmed eyes lifting now and then to survey a passer-by. In the wicker chair with wheels, Grandfather sat silently, his hands crossed over his middle, calm, incurious, at peace. Everywhere birds twittered, butterflies danced, bees hummed lazily over the flowers. It was summertime at Parnassus.

But that particular year, when the family gathered on the lawn, we would sit on the grass and surreptitiously snatch a few dandelions out of the earth to save for Monday's pay.

The things we used to love, we loved no more. Even at night, when Papa would sometimes dress up in a Greek costume and do a native dance which was very gay and called for him to wave a handkerchief over his head and snap his fingers, we would sit apart from the group and make lists of forthcoming chores. None of us could understand how Aphrodite and her brothers could so willingly let week-end dancing and singing and games interfere with their income. There was money to be earned, and such tactics suddenly seemed wasteful and nonproductive to us. One night Cousin Achilles came tripping down the stairs with a sheet wrapped around him and Auntie's switch pinned to his head with a garland of grape leaves. His hairy arms and legs stuck out in all directions as he announced he was a Greek goddess. We thought this rather funny but made no attempt to attack his bare heel, though he egged us on. Our minds were on the pay roll.

Mama thought we were ill because we were losing all sense of humor and childish inclinations, and produced a fresh bottle of Valentine's Meat Juice. But Uncle Demetrius soon observed that we were fast becoming skinflints and curmudgeons of the first water.

One morning when Pericles asked if he could do without his breakfast egg and be paid the price of it instead, Uncle Demetrius looked at my brother long and thoughtfully. In the next moment, as if inspired by the thought of Achilles the night before, I offered to sell my curls for a switch. Uncle Demetrius turned his gaze to me. Artemis was deep in thought, devising some money-making scheme to outbid us all, when my uncle called us to his side at the table.

Putting his arms around us, he then told us the story of King Midas who, given one wish, elected that everything he touched should turn to gold. Poor King Midas! His food turned to gold and he grew thin and starved with hunger. His food and his clothing turned to gold so that he had not a moment's comfort. Even his beautiful daughter turned to gold when he touched her cheek in a fond caress. This, said Uncle Demetrius, was the curse that befell King Midas for his greed.

We were duly impressed, having rather malleable natures, and in a way rather relieved when he added, "And now, my darlings, you have all earned enough money, and I am dismissing you from your jobs before everything you touch turns to gold, which I perceive it is beginning to do in your minds." Then he informed us that the three dollars and seventy cents we had thus far deposited was more than enough to buy us each a lovely present, which he would bring home from California.

And so he did. For Artemis and me, each a beauti-

The Secret Places

THE house at Parnassus was filled with wonderful, lovely, secret places which we never spoke of except among ourselves. They were hidden places—small, intimate, discovered by accident and containing a special, meaningful charm.

For instance, in one of the attic rooms there was a small door, about two feet high, built close to the floor for the purpose of allowing the plumber easy access to his work. Inside this door there was nothing but a jumble of pipes, but there was enough room beneath them and around them to hide our secret treasures, and the space was filled with a collection of minutiae, immeasurably valuable to us. In here we kept some very fine, gold cigar bands, a small box containing a scab which had been peeled intact from Pericles' knee,

one of Artemis' best teeth, several fish eyes which had been cleaned and polished until they gleamed like pearls, a tiny china doll no bigger than a paper match which we had found covered with mud in the vegetable garden, a secret code, an Indian arrowhead, a stone glistening with mica which we were sure was gold and various other treasures—all of incalculable worth to us.

One of the best places was the Scary Place. This was a dark closet at the top of the back stairs leading to the kitchen. It was seldom used and pitch dark, and, more than that, it wound a circuitous passage for about six feet between the walls, the ceiling sloping as it did so to a height of no more than three feet. A few pails, an old broom and some empty boxes were stacked in the front, but for the rest the closet was empty, dark and so narrow that when we sat hunched against the walls our knees touched. It smelled musty in the darkness, and we could feel spider webs as they brushed across our faces and hear strange, creaking sounds in the old floor boards. For some reason, we found it extremely pleasurable to frighten ourselves nearly out of our wits as we huddled in this dark passage, whispering that we heard a moan, smelled blood or felt a skeletal bone on the floor. Here we told ghost stories so bloodcurdling and secrets so dark they must be whispered in stealthy tones. And here we made pacts of loyalty, pledging a solemn oath never to reveal that it was Pericles who dropped Uncle Demetrius' watch and broke the crystal, Artemis who said "Shut up" under her breath to Thea and I who left the pasture gate open so that all the cows wandered off down the road.

A wonderfully Cool Place was the wine cellar. Here the walls were lined with bottles lying one upon the other on shelves so that only the shiny, cylindrical, green glass bottoms showed, giving the room a shimmery, iridescent, undersea effect all around. The floor was cement, and in the middle of the room huge barrels were pyramided, filled with wine and plugged and dated. The room smelled slightly sour, a cool, musty odor of fermentation, and it was always rather damp. We loved to come down here on hot days and walk barefoot, sometimes playing that we were underwater creatures who had found a cave beneath the sea.

There was a Listening Place in the spare room where we sometimes slept, and this, being directly above the dining room, served as an admirable post for gleaning information generally considered too adult for our young ears. A pipe ran from the dining room, up through the spare room and on to the floors above, and simply by sitting on the floor near the pipe, we could hear clearly every word that was spoken as the grownups sat over their coffee.

Here we learned that Cousin Demosthenes was interested in a beautiful, blond Greek girl of unassailable virtue named Evangeline (whom we called the Angel because of her pink and white perfection), and this pleased Auntie very much. Whenever Aphrodite mentioned anybody named Bob or Jim or Harry or some other such Anglo-Saxon name, my aunt grew silent and rather cool. But if a name like Demos or Jason or Evangelos came up, she was all questions and interest. From Aphrodite we heard lots of interesting arguments, which were mostly pro-American and anti-Greek.

There was always something interesting to hear about Cousin Aphrodite. She was either in tears about not being allowed to go out alone with some young man or in ecstatic joy over being granted the privilege. And, of course, there was the subject of her career, which, until the Metropolitan gave it the nod, included all kinds of side issues such as morals, prudence, propriety, motherhood, wifeliness, fastidiousness and refinement.

One of the best things we heard was that Uncle Miltiades was in love with Papa's secretary, and when Grandmother heard the news she collapsed. She lay on the floor and screamed so long that Uncle Miltiades promised never to see the girl again. Mama said it was a pity, he was tied to his mother's apron strings, and she thought it was a wonderful thing for a young girl to learn to be a secretary, thus earning Pin Money and the Right To Come and Go as she pleased. Aristotle said if the secretary wanted to, she could sue Grandmother for alienation of affections. At the Listening Place we learned many things which we afterward discussed in the Scary Place.

There was another place which I had alone and to myself and which I never revealed to anyone, not even Artemis or Pericles—and this was the Crying Place. It was under the porch, a cool, dim, lattice-enclosed area with a dirt floor and a few straggly vines and determined weeds struggling for existence within its shaded portals. I began by feeling sorry for the vines and weeds, thinking of them as abandoned orphans of nature and sprinkling them from a watering can from time to time. As this did no good at all, and the weeds and vines continued to slump miserably, I came to look upon the whole small area as a place of sadness. In here I stored everything I felt sorry for: a Teddy bear with one glass eye and no arms, a doll with a cracked face and torn clothing, who had once sat pristinely under a Christmas tree—each stiff curl in place, her dress a miracle of pink silk—a broken wooden horse, his flying tail gone and one hoof lost forever, even dead bees and butterflies, grasshoppers found lying on their backs, stilled forever in the summer sun, and occasionally wilted flowers. In time the collection became enormous, for dolls were always breaking and being tossed aside, and Mama thought stuffed animals were dust catchers and discarded them the minute their soft coverings became soiled. I even felt sorry for a pitcher someone had thrown away because the handle was broken off, and carried it to the retreat, there to regain its lost dignity.

This haven for the lost and the lonely soon became a kind of Wailing Wall for me whenever I felt cast out by harsh words or abandoned by those I loved. Immediately I would make a beeline for the place under the porch, there to weep my eyes out as I clutched a broken doll or a torn and dirty rabbit to my bosom. If misery loves company, I had plenty of it, for, as I dug muddy fists into my eyes, I was surrounded by the naked and the dead.

One day we came upon a rather astonishing fact. As we were coming down the steps from the third floor, we discovered that one of the treads was loose, and to our amazement we found that by prying a few loose nails away we could lift it up in its entirety. There beneath the tread was a secret place, a dark space about three feet long and one foot wide. But to our complete astonishment, it was not empty! Instead, it contained a dirty, mildewed paper box in which were a secret code, some fine, gold cigar bands, a stone glistening with mica and an Indian arrowhead. On the outside of the box, written in crayon, was the following warning under a drawing of a skull and crossbones: KEEP OUT! PRIVATE! THIS IS THE PROPERTY OF APHRODITE ACHILLES DEMOSTHENES AND ARISTOTLE.

Christmas at Parnassus

AT CHRISTMASTIME Uncle Demetrius flung the ninth
Rule of Conduct to the winds. Decorations, presents,
food—all were lavish. Even the snow, which always
seemed to fall at Christmas in my childhood, fell ex-
travagantly, covering the whole countryside and bank-
ing the evergreen trees until their branches could hold
no more. It was a day of opulence, everything so
much more so than other days—glittering, tinsel-
decked, gilt-edged.

Perhaps because the house was large, perhaps because it was so filled with people, perhaps only because we were so young did Christmas in those lovely,
lost days at Parnassus seem entirely magic. From
morning until night we lived in a dream. And the
dream was golden, filled with presents and lights and

180

candies and sleigh bells and white snow and music and laughter and joy.

The first sight of the tree, standing from floor to ceiling in the parlor, was magic in itself. It glittered with silver, it was festooned with ropes of sparkling gold, and the whole thing flickered with hundreds of flames from tiny candles. From its branches hung little cornucopias filled with candies, and wonderful, shimmering ornaments so intricate and delicately made they were like jewels. I remember a silver boat from which a fairy rose with a glittering wand. There was a glass house with colored windows and a door that opened and closed, a beautiful, pale-blue swan with golden wings and colored bells, painted with flowers, that tinkled when you touched them. I always looked for and loved a little girl made of paper who clutched a rabbit to her silver-spangled breast. I think someone had cut her from an Easter card and begun a long tradition of hanging her on the tree. All the ornaments were hung year after year so that they were lovely and familiar and dear to us: a pink angel with spangled skirts—a blown-glass reindeer green as emeralds—a small, white woolly lamb and, strangely, a tiny Chinaman with yellow, silken coat and black slippers.

The floor under the tree was heaped with presents, big ones, little ones, the packages piled and massed until there was hardly room to move. And always, always, without fail, as much a part of Christmas as the tree itself, there were two dolls.

These sat pristinely under the tree—a blond doll for

Artemis, a brunette doll for me. They had round eyes of glass that opened and closed and pink cheeks and smiling, dimpled mouths. Their hair was curled and beribboned, and they wore party dresses of silk and white socks and little, white kid shoes. How beautiful they were! And how our hearts exploded with love as they held out their arms under the tree.

To compensate for the dolls, Pericles always had an unwrapped present, too—a sled or an Indian suit or something dear to the hearts of boys—but for me, the first sight of the tree with my dolly sitting beneath it, holding out her stiff, little arms, was the supreme moment of Christmas.

It was a tradition at Parnassus that the children were allowed to open their presents first. This was as much a law of survival as a kindly intention, for there were so many people and so many presents that until ours were out of the way there would not have been room for the grownups. However, before we were allowed to go in and begin the mad plunge into the packages, we had to stand with all the others in the octagonal reception hall and sing while Thea, in her black taffeta, accompanied us on the piano.

"*Adeste Fideles*," we sang, as she thumped away at the chords. She was always happy at Christmas, considering it, strangely, an American custom. As she played I looked around the hall. It was early morning and the chandelier was lighted so that with the magic flickering of the tree the house was aglow with lights. The bronze fringe, hanging from the balcony, was intertwined with creeping cedar so that with the colored balls and golden acorns it made a magnificent wreath above our heads. The stairway was festooned with ropes of green, too, and branches of holly made enormous bouquets in all the vases.

The house was warm and smelled of pine as the fire crackled away, and outside beyond the windows sky and earth were white. From the kitchen there drifted the smell of breakfast cooking—bacon and sausage, homemade rolls and fried zucchini squash all mingled with something sweet, the sap from the branches that roared in the fire, the bowls of Jordan almonds that were always part of Christmas and the fragrance of red roses massed on the piano.

As we sang my heart swelled. Thea went from "*Adeste Fideles*" into the gayer, more lilting "Deck The Halls With Boughs Of Holly," swaying from side to side at the piano, her little black-buttoned shoe madly peddling. When it came to the trilling tra-la-la-la, -la-la-la-la, her fingers curled swiftly over the keys. I liked to watch the men when they sang the bass. They put their chins down as far as possible and frowned. Mama's voice always rang clear and sweet above everyone else's, and she always smiled when she sang, holding her hands clasped in front of her.

When the singing was over, the servants and hired hands all trooped in, and Uncle Demetrius presented each with an envelope and shook hands while Auntie dipped into a special wicker basket and brought forth a package for each. It always seemed to take forever to perform this ritual, and Artemis and Pericles and I would stand through it in torment, our eyes glued to the parlor.

When we were at last allowed to dash in, Mama always called after us not to touch the candles, not to sit on the drafty floor and not to eat the candy before breakfast. All the time we tore the paper from our presents, the grownups sat near by, gasping with delight as we held up each treasure from Santa.

I do not know whether we received too many toys, whether we were surfeited with gifts, whether such indulgence turned our heads. Thea always said so, sitting by and folding what paper she could retrieve and winding the ribbon which she always pressed for the next year.

"May you never have less," she would say, shaking her head.

Unimpressed with the possibility of lean years ahead, we exclaimed for joy as each new gift was revealed. And to be sure, in the faraway years to come we often had less. But I do not believe any of us accepted this with less grace because in our childhood we knew the bountifulness of Christmas.

And there was the joy of giving, too, presents we devised ourselves and gave with our hearts. There was a beautiful black-and-orange moth I found lying dead on the porch one morning and saved for Demosthenes—a pink satin pocketbook I made for Aphrodite by sewing two pieces of material together and gathering the top with a drawstring—for Auntie, a rooster feather, carefully wrapped—and for Mama, an empty medicine bottle filled with talcum powder mixed with water. One Christmas Pericles gave Papa a metal ring with a red stone that came in a box of Cracker Jack, and Papa said it was magnificent and wore it on his watch chain all day long. We loved to give these presents and felt that they were received with pure and unadulterated joy as the grownups exclaimed, *"Just what I wanted!"* or *"Isn't it lovely!"*

After breakfast we went to church for the Christmas service, and then before dinner all the relatives began arriving. Ma-Ma would come, leaning on the arms of her two sons, Epimandes and Miltiades with Maritza hurrying anxiously near by. Aunt Eurydice and Uncle Themistocles and Uncle John with his wife and small son, John Paul, would appear, and sometimes a friend of Thea's named Miss Beebee, who was as old and shriveled as a Greek olive and entirely alone in the world. Also, there was often a niece of Grandfather's named Proxithea, who fascinated us because when she ate she always curled her little finger in an exceedingly genteel way.

The reception hall would fill with people as they came stamping in, their coats spangled with snow, their faces ruddy with cold. Uncle Demetrius whisked all about, pouring wine, displaying gifts, hopping up and down to poke the fire.

We could see the dining-room table, heavy with silver and crystal, on which there would soon be placed a whole suckling pig with an apple in its mouth. I remember marveling at the beautiful sight when we sat down to eat, for the table seemed to glitter as the candlelight caught the gleam of silver and twinkled on each glass filled with ruby-red wine. In the center of the table the epergne was filled with fruit, the suckling pig was magnificent on its silver platter in a bed of parsley, and I thought my family entirely beautiful as they raised their glasses in toast after toast of good cheer.

Even today, when I think back, the memories are gilded. They come back like colors in a kaleidoscope, all bright, jumbled, mirrored with light. Christmas was a shining thing.

In the afternoon everyone trooped outside to skate or sit on the birch bridge that curved over the frozen pond and watch the brightly clad figures glide by. The men wore stocking caps and mufflers in gay colors, and Cousin Aphrodite always had a beautiful skating costume of velvet trimmed with fur. They laughed and called to one another and sang as they swept by arm in arm, their knees bent a little, their bodies inclined forward. Round and round they went, while we stumbled by the side until Cousin Demosthenes or Achilles or Aristotle would swoop down on us and catch us up in the swift cadence. Sometimes we fell, but it was of no moment. Instantly we were swept up again, and I remember the sharp thrill of exhilaration as the world slid by in a wide, white circle.

After the skating there was always bobsledding, and it was the same kind of thrill as, clutched in the arms of one of our cousins, we seemed to fly through white space in one intoxicating sweep of motion.

And best of all there were the sleigh rides at night

when Mercury, the beautiful, dark-red sleigh, decorated with the golden wings of the god of speed, was brought out and hitched to the horses. Then, with bells ringing and hoofs clopping, we would dash through the dark and icy cold while Uncle Demetrius, looking like Santa himself in his red stocking cap and his white beard, would snap the whip with a great flourish. Away we would go, sleigh bells ringing, hearts singing, and behind us the octagonal house rose like an enormous Christmas tree against the dark night sky. For all its lights were glowing, and from the many windows, from the top of the small, colored cupola to the broad base of the lower floors, they shone like golden ornaments that grew smaller and smaller as we drove away.

How beautiful it was—a storybook Christmas, so filled with happiness and love that even after I was tucked in bed that night and closed my eyes, I felt like a star on the tree as I hugged my new dolly to my heart.

One Woman's Opinion

As I LOOK back it seems to me we were the mildest of children, totally lacking in criminal instincts and devoid of any underlying symptoms of juvenile delinquency.

I often find myself attributing this to the fact that we did not have comic books in those days, and such horrible stories of crime and atrocity were never brought to our attention. Smugly I tell myself that we were properly brought up, and such vicious vituperations of the human mind would never be permitted in *our* home. The newspaper comic strips which we loved and saved to read over and over on rainy days in the attic were "Bringing Up Father," "Polly And Her Pals," "S'Matter Pop?" and "Mutt and Jeff." These were always comic, as comics were meant to be, and ended with one or more of the characters falling backward out of the picture, his feet in the air.

But I am forced to admit there were some pretty atrocious atrocities handed down to us by way of Greek mythology. For instance, when Polyphemus, the one-eyed Cyclops, discovered Odysseus and some warriors in his cave, he seized two of the men, dashed out their brains and ate them raw. Furthermore, he trapped the remaining men in the cave and the next night cracked two more skulls together, making yet another meal of raw flesh. Odysseus settled the whole matter by getting the Cyclops drunk and then plunged a sharp-pointed, red-hot pole into his eye.

We learned of a terrible, fire-breathing monster called Chimaera, who was a lion in front, a dragon behind and a goat in the middle—and of Echidna, half woman, half snake. And it is certainly doubtful if there has ever been, in all comic-book history, a character more repulsive than the frightening Medusa, who was shaped like a woman, but who had huge, black wings and brazen claws and writhing snakes for hair. Whosoever looked at her was turned to stone.

Yes, but strangely they made little or no impression on us. Perhaps it was because Greek mythology has a fairly-tale quality, concerns itself with unreal people and belongs to an ancient age. There was nothing to emulate as there is in many of the current comic books. We could only pretend, and, after all, it is rather taxing to pretend your middle is a goat. I only know we listened to these tales, found them mildly interesting and could hardly wait to get on with *Hans Brinker And The Silver Skates.*

Not so our American friends. They loved these

tales, which were all new to them, and used to plague
us to tell them over and over while they shuddered
with delight. There were several of these friends
whose names I can still recall: Catherine Carr and
Mae Cabinie (her father was a detective, but she
could not hold a candle to us when it came to real
cloak and dagger stuff) and a boy named Moulton
Dowler and his brother, Shreve. And there was another boy with a fascinating name which I find irresistible, Sterling Schein. There was Kenneth Dane
and Flora Dane and a girl named Puddin' Pomeroy.

Puddin' was all pink and white with pale-blue,
myopic eyes and golden curls, and her mother was
even more protective than Mama, forbidding her ever
to make mud pies or go barefoot or climb trees. Con-
sequently, we never invited her to Parnassus where
such sports were run of the mill.

One day it came to pass, however, that Puddin'
Pomeroy came to Parnassus. Under what circumstances I no longer recall—I only know that she was
there and by her presence enforced upon us all a pro-
longed boredom.

Partly because Mama had taught us that to be a
good host or hostess was a vital part of life, partly to
protect her from trees, mud and broken glass—all
threats to life and limb, as Mrs. Pomeroy had warned
us—we took her into the house to play. Mrs. Pomeroy
was a big, large-boned woman with yellow hair and
tiny eyes and a voice like a cement mixer, and we
would not have dreamed of disobeying her orders.
Therefore we took Puddin' inside and kept her there,

trying to entertain her with whatever was at hand. According to our lights it was a normal, indoor afternoon, rather boring, and we were glad to see the last of Puddin' when her mother came to fetch her home.

But, alas, for Mrs. Pomeroy it was an afternoon of sedition, corruption and lunacy from which she snatched her child in the nick of time. This is the letter she wrote to Mama:

Dear Madam:

I have considered taking this matter to the Authorities, but my husband, a man of extreme kindness and delicacy, has advised me against it. Therefore, I wish to make it *perfectly clear* to you that I do not wish my daughter to associate with your family in *any wise,* in future.

I have been *sick abed* since the afternoon Priscilla spent at your sister's home in Webster Groves as her *shocking* experience has had a *shattering effect* on my nerves. It is not my wish to point out to you, Madam, a mode of behavior and family life which we who *love* our children attempt to provide for them, but it is *clearly advisable* to *warn* you that *if you continue* as you are, measures will be taken.

I understand your niece keeps a skeleton in her bedroom, that you and your sister comport yourselves in costumes and read fortunes and that an old woman is forced to sleep in a chest of drawers. Priscilla has told me of an escape tunnel in the basement and that she was shown a cage in which live animals are kept for inspection as well as flats of *poisonous toadstools.* I do not know why a dirty yellow dog is kept on the premises as well as a *prowling beast* with a strange name. I can only tell you, Madam, how horrified I was when Priscilla confided to me that at nap time the children were put to bed with the most *shocking* stories of *lewdness, immorality* and *vice*. Again I say, were it not for my husband's *extreme delicacy* of nature, I would have you before the Authorities *at once*. However, let this serve as a warning, Madam, to *stay away* from innocent children.

When Mama read this letter to Auntie, they both laughed so hard that tears ran down their faces. Mama could not get over the old woman who slept in a chest of drawers, and when she tried to read the part about the prowling beast again, she had to put the letter down, so overcome with laughter was she.

But after a few days she did not think it was so funny and wanted to call up Mrs. Pomeroy and give her a piece of her mind, but Papa, who also had delicacy of nature, forbade her to do it.

"She's just a ridiculous old fool," he said. "To answer her letter would be beneath you."

"Very well," said Mama. "But just imagine! She thinks we're crazy!"

"Exactly," said Papa and, resorting to French, he added, *"Qui s'excuse s'accuse,"* which means "He who excuses himself, accuses himself."

Besides the stories of *lewdness, immorality* and *vice* which fell upon Puddin' Pomeroy's ears at Parnassus, we were also told other stories, and, having little in common with the disposition of a woman like Mrs. Pomeroy, I know not whether these would have offended her as well.

Auntie told them to us—they were stories of her grandmother's life (our great-grandmother), which had been told to her when she was a child, and, of course, they consisted of parts of Auntie's girlhood as well. They were exciting, thrilling, filled with adventure and romance, and in one of them Auntie told us our own grandmother was hidden in a huge oil jug during a skirmish between the Russians and the Turks. There was also a terrifying lady midwife, who smoked cigarettes and glared at little children, and many other characters, some of them our own relatives, who were strange and new to us.

Auntie could tell a story like no one else in the world. She took her time and filled her tales with the most fascinating detail and description, and she had a marvelous flair for suspense, so that no matter how many times we heard these stories, we always sat breathless when Auntie came to the part where a gypsy lurked toward Grandmother's house or a Turk stood with a sword held to Great-grandmother's breast. When Auntie was seventy years old, she wrote all these stories down in a book called *And Across Big Seas*, which is available in the bookstores today and is, naturally, one of my most prized possessions. They were all told to her by her grandmother, the one who taught Mama to read the cup, and Auntie got the title from one of the fortunes which said the family would sail across big seas.

No matter how many stories we heard from Auntie or read in books, if Mama was on hand when bedtime came around, she always sent us off to slumberland with a few of her own. Combining pleasure with learning, Mama always gleaned them from the store of Greek mythology which was at her fingertips and soothed us as we went off to dreamland with tales of the gods and goddesses who swallowed their children whole, drove people mad, cast men into the sea and women into Hades. We listened while stories of wrath, vengeance, pride, vanity and even promiscuity among the immortals fell upon our ears.

Darling Mama, who would fire a servant without a moment's notice if she heard us being told about a bogeyman, thought absolutely nothing of relating to us the story of Tityus.

This giant, it seems, had insulted Apollo's mother. Apollo was so annoyed that he hurled Tityus down to Tartarus, far below Hades, where his huge bulk covered nine acres and his liver was exposed for the vultures to pick. As if this were not enough, Apollo further ordained that the liver should have the peculiar ability to constantly renew itself so that Tityus' torment was eternal.

And she told us about Tantalus.

Tantalus, in a fit of pique, cooked his son and served the body at a banquet. When the gods learned of this, they were so outraged that they cast him down to Hades, there forever to remain standing up to his neck in water which would recede when he tried to drink and surrounded by food which was snatched away when he attempted to eat.

"And that is where we get our word tantalize," said Mama, throwing in a lesson in etymology.

I always thought it was only right that Tantalus should have been punished for eating his son, until I discovered that one of the gods had been guilty of a far greater transgression along the same lines and had gone scot free.

Cronus, fearing one of his children might someday usurp his throne, the sky, swallowed each one whole as it was born. By the time the sixth child, Zeus, came into the world, his wife was so upset she handed Cronus a stone wrapped in swaddling clothes which he swallowed instead. In time, this unappetizing morsel sat so heavily on his stomach that he was forced to disgorge the whole brood, one by one. For this, as well as the crime of mutilating his own father with a sickle, Cronus went free as a lark.

When Mama decided the hour was growing late, she would tuck us in, give us each a kiss and wish us sweet dreams.

"Now go straight to sleep, darlings," she would say, "before you turn into Chinamen."

With sweet thoughts of tantalizing torture, cooked children and long queues in place of our curls, we would listen to the katydids and watch the moon drift behind a dark cloud and smell the honeysuckle that filled the night air and drift off to dreamland. . . .

First Love

THE day was very warm and oppressed by that queer silence that seems to be a part of extreme heat. Even the pond was still, a yellowish light seeming to shimmer above it, and the cattails which grew by its side were tall and silent. Just over the surface of the water, tiny gnats and water insects filled the air with a kind of frenetic and meaningless motion.

Two rowboats, shaped like swans, sat moored to their trappings under the birch bridge that curved over the pond. One was called Zephyrus, for the wind, and the other Amphritite, for the wife of Neptune. Immobile in the dead calm, they sat like two great white birds, indifferent to the stout ropes that hindered their flight, oblivious of the sun that blazed mercilessly down on their proud, curved necks and their folded, carved white wings.

All of Parnassus was lulled into a kind of passive resistance by the heat. The trees were motionless and the air itself was like a wall. Life and a kind of death seemed to go on simultaneously. Flowers bloomed in their beds but the earth around them was caked and dry. In the unnatural stillness, butterflies flew from blossom to blossom. Everything seemed at a standstill, as if waiting, and except for an occasional sound or movement, the place seemed deserted. Somewhere, far away, a cow mooed—a lonely, mournful sound—and the workmen in the fields had patches of dark blue on their light blue shirts where perspiration had soaked through.

I sat by the edge of the pond, my chin on my knees, chewing a blade of grass. One of the hired men came down the road, coaxing a herd of cattle toward the pasture. He carried a stick in his hand and made occasional gruff, rather meaningless sounds calculated to keep the animals in line. I noticed a bull among the cows and automatically pulled my dress down to my shoe tops to cover my scarlet socks, for Auntie had told us bulls always became enraged by the color red.

I was alone. Artemis and Pericles, as well as all the grownups, were asleep in their rooms where they had gone to find relief from the heat in napping. I could imagine them all, lying on their beds like rag dolls, limp, lifeless, with hearts and minds of sawdust. I, who had refused the temporary surcease of sleep, preferred to sit alone on the bank of the pond, chewing my blade of grass and watching the retreating behinds of cows as they ambled down the road, swinging their ropy tails.

For I was in love. I lay back on the grass, looking up at the blue sky, and thought about this. I had been in love once before, but now that I was nine this seemed a faraway, empty love compared to the surge of panic whenever I saw Campbell Garrett.

This handsome young man with the pretentious name was in his twenties—a college friend of Aristotle's. Whenever he came out to play tennis I was overcome with shyness and hung my head and fled to a safe distance where I could watch him without being seen. When he rumpled my curls or called me Snicklefritz or tossed me a flash of his white teeth in his tanned face, I would blush and squirm. But away from him, I planned a whole life during which Campbell Garrett was practically never off his knees.

Now I leaned back on the grass, resting on my elbows and made a mouth like Gloria Swanson. This was accomplished by lifting the upper lip high off the front teeth and holding it there. Campbell Garrett was on his knees, protesting his love as I idly stroked his hair.

"But I must go on with my career," I said.

"Then let me go with you," he begged.

This was too easy. I gave up the career and decided to have consumption. I was dying. Campbell Garrett was on his knees by my bedside.

"You mustn't die!" he wept. "I can't go on without you!"

I reached out a thin white hand and touched his cheek, haggard with grief. I was too frail, too close to death to speak. Lying on the grass, two real tears rolled down my cheeks as I thought of the irony of it all. To have loved so deeply and then to have been stricken by an incurable disease. Feebly, I reached out again and he kissed my hand, overcome with emotion as I passed out of this world.

I now moved to a brand-new stage. I was on a runaway horse, dashing madly toward the edge of a cliff. Behind me I heard roaring hoofbeats and everything turned black as Campbell dragged me back from the precipice in the nick of time. Immediately he sank to his knees in gratitude as he stroked my hair. . . . When I recovered from this excruciating experience, I decided on a new one. Another man was in love with me—a millionaire who showered me with diamonds and furs. Campbell Garrett, once more on the bend, pleaded with me not to sell out for jewels but to marry him for love instead. Foolishly I refused and the millionaire turned false, leaving me to waste away in an attic. Then, as I sat coughing and sewing, who should return but Campbell, again in an attitude of genuflexion, to take me away from it all!

This was a lovely way to spend the afternoon and I lived each scene to the hilt—crying, coughing, breathing heavily. . . . Once I even took off my shoes and socks and went down to the pond and walked out up to my calves during a suicide sequence when I heard Campbell was dead. The fact that Artemis came running across the road at just that moment did nothing to help.

"What are you doing?" she cried. "You know you're not supposed to go in the water!"

This was absurd. I was not going to drown, as my lover was about to approach in a motorboat.

"I'm not doing anything," I said.

"You are too! You're in the water!"

"Well, I was hot."

"You're not supposed to," she said, being a child of great moral rectitude. "You know Mama said that. Now come on out. Thea made some lemonade!"

We walked back to the house together and for the first time I felt rather alien and distant toward my sister. What did she know about life? I had just been through consumption, starvation in a garret and suicide while she slept peacefully, aware only of a world of lemonade and rules. It annoyed me that her crowded world was so shallow while mine, marked by the hills and dales of passion and suffering, was peopled by only Campbell and me.

"Remember Wallace Reid?" I asked suddenly.

"Yes," she said.

"I used to think he was wonderful. Of course I was young then, but I thought he was wonderful. Didn't you?"

"Oh, I still think he's nice," said Artemis generously. She added: "Except he's a movie star. Who wants to be in love with a movie star?"

"I didn't say anything about being in love with him," I said irritatedly. "I just said I used to think he was wonderful."

"Well, I'll tell you something if you won't tell," said

Artemis suddenly, stopping and putting her hands behind her back. "Promise?"

"I promise."

"Well, I saw Aphrodite's beau. He came to see Mama at our house. They talked and I was in the hall and I saw him!"

"Well what of it?" I asked. "What if you did see him?"

Her eyes grew round and filled with that shining, naïve wonder that was so much a part of her.

"He looks just like a movie star, Ariadne," she confided. "You ought to see him. He has brown eyes and brown curly hair and the whitest teeth and two dimples when he smiles."

"Did he smile at you?"

"No. They didn't know I was there. But this is what I wanted to tell you, only you have to promise not to tell."

"I promise."

"Word of honor?"

"Word of honor."

"Well, today when I was supposed to be taking a nap I thought about him the whole time. I didn't go to sleep once."

"You DIDN'T?"

"No."

After a time she said, "I'll bet you think that's silly."

"No, I don't," I said.

We walked hand in hand into the house.

Last Love

THE situation was grave at Parnassus. Auntie's dark-
est predictions had come true, and Aphrodite had
fallen in love with a young American medical student
who was in her class at the university.

"This was bound to happen," said Auntie stoically,
madly planning trips to Greece and other distant parts
of the world which would remove her daughter from
the threat of the young man, who was of German descent and very, very handsome indeed. (Ah, Mama,
a fig for your fortunes! You and Aphrodite were in
cahoots long before the news was out!)

She had very little idea of what she was up against,
however, for Aphrodite in love was Aphrodite of the
myths, who, when separated from Adonis, caused the
world to grow bleak and cold, but, while with him,
the birds to sing and the flowers to bloom.

202

Auntie got nowhere with her trips and so, as a final resort, filled the house with as many Greek men as possible, hoping that one would capture her daughter's heart and cause the American to topple from his throne. Aphrodite scorned them all, although she thought it rather clever when Spyros Skouras, home from the war, flew a cub plane over the grounds and dropped theater tickets weighted with stones down to the family. They came wafting down and settled on the lawn, and Auntie made a great to-do over the ingenuity of the Hellenic mind. Aphrodite just smiled her new, gentle smile.

I had not seen Aphrodite's beau because from the beginning Auntie refused to allow him to come to the house, and their romance had flowered in the musty halls of the medical school or as they worked together in the laboratory. When Auntie got wind of it, she put her foot down, and I realized what Aphrodite meant when she told Jenny Brentwood, "When it comes to things like that, Mama is made of stone."

Now when Aphrodite went off to school in the mornings, driving the new Chandler, Auntie watched her go, as Clytemnestra must have watched her daughter Iphigenia depart to be sacrificed at Aulis. She gazed after her with eyes in which fear and sorrow were mingled.

One morning I wakened early before anyone else was stirring and tiptoed downstairs to walk barefoot in the wet grass, a thing I loved to do. At this hour of dawn the world is still misty with dew and the sun just begins to edge the leaves with gold. One by one, birds began to twitter, making, at first, a tiny, tentative sound, a chirp here, an answering chirp there. I felt an immense, overwhelming privacy as I walked over the wet grass alone, for it seemed there was no one else on earth, only I, and this gives one a great, limitless power as well as personal dignity.

I walked everywhere, seeing everything in the pale, early light, aware of a kind of hushed immobility. The arbor was covered with pink roses, their petals still wet with dew, and the flowers stood in their gardens in a kind of breathless stillness. All was quiet. Only the birds twittering made any sound.

Down in the vegetable garden a blue border of cornflowers was hazy in the mist. A tomato, hanging from its vine, shone bright and wet against the green leaves. Clusters of purple grapes, covered with a silvery film, hung still as paintings, almost artificial in the early light. In the darkened barn the grindstone stood motionless, the cows stared stolidly, now and again whisking a fly off their rumps with dispassionate tails. The coach and surrey were empty and seemed abandoned. Around the pond nothing stirred.

I wandered all over the grounds in my nightgown. The grass was studded with fragrant white clover blossoms like little stars, and the air had a fresh, clean, night smell, just beginning to be warmed by sun. When I looked back at the house far away across the lawn, it seemed to rise in a cloud of mist, unreal, fairylike, all the shades drawn so that it had a remote, closed look.

I stood looking at it, and, though I was then only

about ten years old, a great sadness came over me because it seemed to me that this was the way my Auntie looked lately—closed and shut and all the happiness and light gone out. And I realized suddenly that I hadn't heard her laugh in a long, long time.

I hurried back and went inside and crawled into bed. Then I heard Aphrodite say, "Where have you been, Ariadne?"

"Nowhere," I said.

"Of course you've been somewhere. Where did you go?"

"Outside. Why aren't you asleep?"

She sat up. "Outside! What were you doing outside. Let me see you." She came over and felt my feet. They were wet and the bottom of my nightgown was damp. "You're going to catch cold," she said. "Come and get in bed with me."

I climbed in beside her.

"Now what were you doing?" she asked, pulling my feet against her.

I considered this and then decided to tell her.

"Well, sometimes I go for a walk in the morning. *You* know, just walk around . . . It's nice out, and you feel like nobody else is in the world but you. It's a nice feeling and kind of sad, too. . . ."

"You little monkey," she said, rumpling my hair. "What do you think about?"

"Oh . . . things."

"Things like what?"

"Things like romance."

"Romance! What do you know about romance?"

I looked at her curiously. "Why, I know a lot. Why does Auntie want you to marry a Greek?"

She smiled. "Oh . . . now look here. Have you been listening to the grownups?"

"Yes. Sometimes. I heard her tell Mama you wouldn't be happy married to an American. Wouldn't you?"

After a moment she said, "Yes, I think I would."

"Then why won't Auntie let you?"

"Now hush," she said. "You go back to sleep. You mustn't think about things like that."

Just then a rooster crowed, sending out a bugle call of greeting as the sun blazed in the sky. I felt very tired and closed my eyes.

"I'm going to marry an American," I said. "I'm not going to marry a Greek. I'm going to marry an American doctor, like you, and if anybody tries to stop me, I'll run away. They'll come and get me and lock me in a tower, but I'll escape and then I'm going to sail away and live with the doctor in a foreign land. If he does anything I don't like, I'll run away again and go and live in Chicago." (This turned out to be substantially true, as it happened.) "Why don't you do that?"

"You're a funny baby," said Cousin Aphrodite, giving me a hug. "Now go to sleep."

"All right," I said, and closed my eyes.

It was not until a few days later that I saw my cousin's beau when he came driving up to the house and went inside to have a talk with Auntie and Uncle Demetrius. Artemis had certainly been right the day she said she saw him and he looked exactly like a movie star. He was tall and thin with brown hair and eyes, very handsome and, as he went into the house, very stern. I had overheard Aphrodite tell Auntie that he insisted on having a talk with her parents as he considered her mother's refusal to see him absurd. He was going to settle the matter once and for all, especially as to his intentions as an honorable man. Therefore, when he marched into the house I saw no dimples such as Artemis had raved over.

But when he came out he was all smiles and handsomer than ever, and Auntie did not look quite so formidable and even shook hands with him.

After that everything began to change. I understood that Auntie was admitting defeat, for after talking with him she relented considerably and relinquished many of her demands on Aphrodite. In a way it was sad. It was like seeing the Parthenon crumble. But, on the other hand, love is a wondrous thing and casts its light on all who are near. Auntie was softening in spite of herself.

For a while she clung tenaciously to a few demands. That they wait, that they think it over, that they make a final decision after graduation. Perhaps she still hoped that in the interlude a Greek would come along with all the attributes of this fine young man, but I heard her admit to Mama that such a person would be hard to find.

After this all was right with the world at Parnassus. Auntie was happy, Aphrodite was happy and Mama just said, "Oh, it's all nonsense," when Auntie remembered, and announced triumphantly, that the cup had been right again. For in the end she was very, very pleased to announce the engagement of her daughter to Armin Hofsommer.

The Ashes of Parnassus

OUR life in St. Louis was very different from the one we led at Parnassus. It was citified and formal, and we were much more proper. Artemis and I wore uniforms to school, and for in-between Mama ordered Peter Pan dresses from Franklin Simon in New York. Pericles wore wool suits with knee-length knickers and always took off his hat when he came in the house. Twice a year we went to Swopes' and bought sturdy shoes for school and black patent-leather shoes for dress-up for Artemis and me.

At dinner we sat primly at our places and were served by a butler. We took music lessons and French lessons and went to Miss Moller's dancing classes, and Mama was always talking about taking us abroad to "finish" us.

Nevertheless, different as it was, so much less care-free and gay, we loved our home, and after a barefoot summer in the sun it was always good to get back and settle down in our own beautiful house.

We had just returned from Parnassus one fall and were sitting at the dining-room table ready to begin our soup when the doorbell rang.

It is odd how momentous events, seeming at the time to happen all at once, kaleidoscoping into a single, jumbled, meaningless disorder, will, upon recollection, form themselves into a series of individual circumstances, each with shape and form.

The doorbell rang, the housemaid went to answer it, there was a kind of swooshing sound in the hall, and all at once Auntie and Uncle Demetrius stood before us. My beautiful auntie was smudged with soot and her hair was awry. She looked old and haggard and her mouth, usually so sweet and mobile, was turned down like an angry wound in her face.

Beside her Uncle Demetrius stood, suddenly very small, very old, somehow clinging to his wife, and his usually animated face was still and bleak. I remember thinking that his beard and waxed mustaches looked false, as if they had been pasted on his face.

We were all sitting with our spoons half raised to our lips in attitudes of stunned surprise, and as I write this I can feel, as if it were happening now, the sudden, physical pain in my stomach as Auntie said in a whisper, "The house has burned to the ground!"

Her words hung suspended in mid-air for a full minute. It was as if a dagger, having been plunged

into our hearts, was then held before our frightened
eyes.

In the next moment all was confusion—chairs
pushed back from the table, questions, answers, tears,
embraces, so much commotion as everyone said over
and over that it could not be true. But it was true.
Auntie and Uncle Demetrius had simply come home
from a shopping trip to the city and found their home
in flames, three quarters of it consumed by fire before
they arrived, the last quarter devoured before their
eyes.

Auntie went into the drawing room and sat down
in her dirty clothes. Her shoulders sagged and she
began to cry. She kept saying, "My home, my beautiful home!" while Uncle Demetrius hovered about her,
occasionally patting her hand and then looking off into
space as if he were dazed.

Somehow she was able to give us a sequence of
events as they happened.

"We got off the train in Webster Groves and I knew
at once that something was wrong. The car was not
there to meet us, and there was a strange milling
around, everyone's eyes seemed to be on us. Then a
stranger came up and said there had been a fire and
he would take us home."

They drove toward the house, Auntie holding
Uncle Demetrius' hand hard, praying it was the barn.

"Was it the barn?" she asked the driver, knowing it
was not.

"No, Mrs. Jannopoulo. It's your house."

Her heart beat like a gong in her chest and her

palms were wet and cold. Uncle Demetrius sat and tapped his foot, bent forward a little as if to help the car in motion. Overhead the sky glowed faintly pink, then red.

When they drove through the gates, they both cried out, an unintelligible sound, and tried to get out of the moving automobile. Flames roared against the sky, and most of the house was gone, leaving a jagged pattern, black and ragged on the horizon.

Auntie said, "I had such a pain in my heart . . ." and put her hands over her breast.

The fire raged, clawing the sky. Now and then, through the flames, they could see what was left of the lower floors. The lawn was full of people, milling around, staring with their faces turned upward. Some held their children high to see. Others were crying.

"My bedroom curtains were all stained and the sleeping porch was gone. . . ." said Auntie, as if this were an important detail. "And then, down below, there was the fern growing in the parlor window between the pink curtains as if nothing were happening. I remember this because in a little while it was gone, too . . ."

The lawn was covered with furniture and bedding and odds and ends. Neighbors had come from everywhere when the alarm sounded and had rushed inside to save what they could.

Auntie said, looking into space, "Such strange things people save when a house is afire—pillows and blankets, picture albums. Someone saved the albums. And records from the victrola . . ."

People were everywhere. They ran about or stood in stunned silence. The firemen called orders to one another and water poured against the flames, but they grew and grew, licking the now-darkened sky and turning it blood red in the night.

Auntie sat, looking at no one, speaking in a monotone, remembering little things. It seemed to me there was no body under her clothes, only a voice. They hung shapeless and disordered. Although her hands in her lap were clasped together, she kept rubbing them, as if she were cold.

"I watched the flames roaring against the sky and destroying my house," she said. "They made it a pitiful sight, with no dignity left. Whatever they touched, they consumed, and the house just stood there defenseless until it was destroyed." She added, as if in afterthought, "Fire makes a terrible sound, like an angry beast."

She and Uncle Demetrius rushed out of the car, but they could not go near the house. The heat was overpowering and all was chaos. She asked wildly about her father and Thea. Both had been out that day as well as her children. Only the servants had been home, and they were safe.

She covered her face with her hands. "It is a terrible sight to see your home burn to the ground. You will never know. It's like watching a death. . . . Ashes flew all through the air, black things like bats, and once I heard a terrible, crashing sound, it must have been a ceiling falling in . . . I don't know. . . . Sparks and pieces of timber flew through the air, and Demetrius was shouting to the firemen and rushing all about, and suddenly I felt this was a dream. . . . Someone, a very kind person, brought me a chair. It was covered with soot, and I tried to recognize it but I could not. Because of this, I was sure I was in a dream. Afterward I realized it was a dining-room chair.

"All the time I sat there I kept looking at the fire. I didn't believe it. . . . One has the strangest thoughts. . . . They told me the house had been burning all day, that it had started from the wiring in the attic, and I thought, I must call the electrician in the morning"

She wanted to go on but could not.

"It is all gone!" she said at last. "There is nothing left, absolutely nothing. . . . Nothing, nothing, only ashes . . ." and her voice sounded faraway, empty and desolate.

Suddenly I, who had gone to stand in a corner of the room with my hands clasped over my heart, felt a sinking sensation, as if I were falling into a bottomless well and darkness were enfolding me. I began to cry. The word gone began to take shape and meaning. The house was gone. If we went back tomorrow there would not be a house. Where it had been there would only be a nothing. If we drove in the driveway and looked ahead, there would only be sky and a huge gap between the trees. There would be no reception hall waiting for us, holding out its arms to enfold us. Where it had been would be emptiness. The house was gone. Everything in it was gone.

"The glass paperweight!" I thought, suddenly remembering the little girl in a flurry of snow, and clapped my hand over my mouth.

Artemis and Pericles came and stood beside me and held my hands and began to cry softly, too. Through our tears we saw the grownups now beginning to fortify themselves to face this tragedy. Mama was busily arranging beds for Auntie and Uncle Demetrius to spend the night and insisting that they eat something. She had always vowed that bread makes bones, but now she was affirming that vegetable soup builds strength. Papa, more to the point, got out a decanter of whisky and poured a stiff drink for Uncle Demetrius and insisted that Auntie have some, too.

Suddenly I heard Artemis say, "Just think! The Billiard Room is gone!" and Pericles added, "I left my chemical set there. It's burned up, now. . . ."

We wept inconsolably as we began to recall all the things that were no more. No one paid any attention to us. The grownups were on a new tack. They were saying how lucky they were, how grateful that no one had been hurt. The German cook had fled with the first sign of flames. It was due to her hysteria and the fact that the water supply was inadequate that the fire had taken such an unprecedented toll. Auntie said over and over, "Thank God the children are safe!" and Mama kept saying it was a lucky thing Grandfather and Thea had both been out. To give each other comfort and courage, they sought out every circumstance to alleviate the loss.

In the meantime whisky and vegetable soup were

consumed, and indeed one or the other did seem to build strength, for as they sat down to the table to finish the rest of the dinner, they were all speaking more coherently and rather excitedly, and Uncle Demetrius was explaining about the wiring, which he was sure had started the trouble. Furthermore, once out of his daze, he began to plan a new house, a more beautiful house, and he and Papa discussed insurance policies.

For once Mama forgot about us and overlooked the fact that we had had no dinner at all. Artemis, Pericles and I simply stood in the drawing room and cried, as lonely and uncomprehending as if we had suddenly become orphans.

"We can't ever slide down the banisters again!" Pericles said.

"Or walk barefoot in the wine cellar," said Artemis.

I remembered my broken dolls and torn stuffed animals in the Crying Place and closed my eyes as I imagined them helpless in the flames.

Artemis said, "It was such a big house to burn down! Every single thing's gone. Just think, the sleeping porch is gone and the spare room and everything! Even little things are gone. Remember the pink shell we used to listen to?"

"And the little girl holding the rabbit on the Christmas tree."

"And the ice box with orange soda . . ."

"And the pressed flowers in the books . . ."

"And the microscope . . ."

"Thea's marriage license . . ."

"All our dress-up clothes in the attic . . ."

"And the billiard cues . . ."

They were all gone, and we would never have them back again, we thought, as we wept miserably and huddled against each other on the couch.

Then Uncle Demetrius, looking up from the dinner table, saw us through the double doors and exclaimed, "My God, just look at those poor children!"

Aghast that she had forgotten us, Mama rushed into the drawing room and propelled us back to the table.

"Oh, my poor children!" she kept saying. "You haven't eaten a bite!" She wiped our faces with a napkin and settled us in chairs. "Now you shall have some nice, hot vegetable soup," she promised, "for it builds strength. And never mind, Uncle Demetrius is going to build a new house, a very beautiful new house, and you shall go back to Parnassus every summer just as before."

Completely unreassured, we began to eat our soup.

Then Uncle Demetrius, bless his darling soul, jumped up from the table and slapped his napkin against his thigh.

"By heaven, I have it!" he cried. "Just the thing! A treasure hunt!" He sat down and explained, calling us to his side, never mind the soup. Uncle Demetrius knew that hope builds strength, too. With his arms around us he painted an exciting picture of adventure and suspense.

"You remember your auntie's jewel box in the fireplace? Well now! It's somewhere in those ashes. Yes, sir! Melted all together, no doubt, but it's there all right. And inside it are her diamonds. And I'll tell you something, darlings. Fire can't destroy diamonds. Now all we have to do is find that mass of molten lead and presto! Auntie has her jewels again.

"Now this is what we'll do. As soon as the ashes have cooled, we'll take a trip out to Parnassus and we'll go on a treasure hunt. We'll dig and dig and search and search. We'll sift every ash, and before long we'll find that box. Yes, sir! A melted iron box full of jewels!"

As he talked our eyes began to widen, and soon we caught the excitement in his voice and were planning with him this wonderful new and thrilling adventure.

And so it was that in the end even the ashes of Parnassus brought joy to our hearts.

Epilogue

THE octagonal house is gone and is no more. True to his promise, Uncle Demetrius let us hunt for weeks through the ashes heaped in the stone foundation until we were as black as chimney sweeps. At last he himself found Auntie's jewel box and her diamonds were retrieved.

Also, true to his promise, he built a new house on the old foundation, but it was never the same. Somewhat smaller but much more efficient, it was two stories high, made of gleaming white stucco and was fresh and clean. All the furniture was new, and everything was up-to-date and modern. We liked to go out and watch it being built, but when it was finished we regarded it as a newcomer and treated it with rather polite diffidence. One would scarcely romp barefoot through a brand-new house, much less tear up a stair tread to look for a secret place. Or perhaps it was just that we were growing older.

There was no bronze fringe around the balcony, no Greek statues on the newel posts. All the books were new and held no secret messages or pressed flowers, and the icebox contained a strange contraption called a Kelvinator and had no tap for orange soda.

Auntie kept her jewelry in a safe, Thea slept in a regular bed with legs on it, and soon after the fire Hercules died and was replaced by two fox terriers named Toots and Brownie. Nothing was the same.

For us, in those early years of childhood, the octagonal house was gone. Yet today I know it is not gone nor ever can be, for it lives in the heart, and there it shall always remain, rising as elaborately and fancifully as it ever did, in the midst of trees and flowers.

The reception hall is there and all its magic rooms are there. The Billiard Room and the Wine Room, Thea's room with its secret bed and the parlor and the pantry and the Medicine Room. The attic rooms, crammed with trunks and toys and treasures, and down, down, down beneath the cellar, beneath the earth itself, entered only through a tunnel, the Storm Room.

It is not gone but lives sweetly undisturbed in the heart. It holds out its arms as compassionately as ever. The little girl in the paperweight is still on the parlor table, standing in a flurry of snow. The pansies and roses and nasturtiums are still pressed between the leaves of books in the Billiard Room. In a box in the

attic wall, arrowheads and cigar bands and a tiny
doll no bigger than a penny match are still safely hidden away. The two bronze figures of Night and Day
still stand proudly on the newel posts of the staircase,
holding their torches aloft and lighting the way above.
Around the balcony a pointed fringe hangs, strung
with colored ornaments and golden acorns, now and
again jangling as presents come hurtling down from
above. Thea's marriage license reposes safely in its
hiding place, orange soda flows eternally sweet and
frosty from a tap in the icebox, nothing is changed.
It is all still there. It awaits only to be recalled to
come back to a heart shaped by its memories.

the end.